Contents

See
Medical Expense Record
at the back of the book.

PREFACE TO THE 13TH EDITION

S INCE the first edition of *How to Cover the Gaps in Medicare* was published in 1983, a virtual revolution has occurred in the Nation's system of health care for senior citizens. The costs of hospitalization, Medicare and supplemental health insurance premiums, and nursing-home care are much more than they were then. Doctors and hospitals now are paid according to Government-mandated price arrangements and are threatened by the Government and insurers with sanctions unless they "cut costs" wherever possible. Conclusive evidence of the full effects of such practices on the quality of patient care is not yet in, but it is clear, for example, that elderly patients are being discharged from hospitals much sooner than ever before.

Whatever the clinical effects of these changes may be, the financial impact on elderly health care consumers of health care price increases over the past 20 years has been dramatic. For example, currently three-fifths of elderly nursing home residents are Medicaid recipients. Indeed, in recent decades the health-related financial problems of America's senior citizens have emphasized the need for elderly individuals and their families to seek a range of options that encompasses both health *and* long-term care if they are to avoid financial ruin.

It would be impossible in a general discussion to describe in great detail all of the ramifications of current health care and long-term-care trends, or all of the opportunities available to people in different circumstances. It is possible, however, to describe the principal considerations that all of us ought to take into account when we plan for our own futures—and when we exercise our rights as citizens in choosing what type of health care "system" will provide widest accessibility to the best medical care at the lowest cost.

Part 1 of this book briefly describes the history and current provisions of Medicare, which have undergone numerous changes in the past decade. It also traces the history of the "medigap"—the portion of elderly health care costs that has not been covered by either Medicare Part A or Part B. Despite all the talk of "cost containment" there is little evidence that the medigap has begun to shrink. On the contrary, the medigap has grown wider and may continue to do so.

1

Part 2 describes Medicare+Choice (M+C) and Medicare supplemental health insurance. M+C allows beneficiaries to choose, subject to availability, among a variety of private, market-based health-care plans similar to those available to the non-Medicare population (e.g., HMOs). This option is discussed in Chapter V. Medicare beneficiaries who choose to remain in the original fee-for-service plan run by the Federal Government should understand and consider purchasing one of the National Association of Insurance Commissioners' ten standardized Medicare Supplemental Insurance policies. Chapters VI, VII, and VIII review these policies and provide criteria for selecting one.

Part 3 discusses long-term care options. Many of the aged understandably are concerned that the costs of long-term care in a nursing home will leave either themselves or their spouses financially destitute. In fact, there are a variety of protections against the costs of such care. Not only have continuing-care and home-care alternatives widened in the past two decades, but changes in Medicaid eligibility rules opened the door to far greater "middle class" participation in that program. Recent legislation has altered some of the rules and penalties relating to transfers of assets in order to become eligible for Medicaid but it is doubtful that these developments will seriously curtail Medicaid eligibility.

Part 4 considers end-of-life decisions that have been necessitated by court rulings relating to "right-to-die" issues. The fact is that your wishes respecting the type and extent of medical care that you receive if you become unable to make your own decisions probably will not be honored unless you follow the specific procedures mandated by the "living will" legislation.

Lastly, an appendix considers some of the issues that have framed the debate over public versus private health care systems, and which promise to attract greater public interest as the costs as well as benefits of public health care become more apparent.

The task of insuring oneself against the risk of illness and the vicissitudes of old age is growing increasingly complex. At the same time, the risks of *not* insuring oneself are more threatening than ever. It is our hope that the pages that follow will be useful as an introductory guide to obtaining whatever protection is available.

Part 1
THE MEDICARE QUANDARY

I.

THE HEALTH INSURANCE PRINCIPLE

A S with other forms of insurance, the purpose of health insurance is to reduce the financial burden of risk by dividing losses among many individuals. In general, health insurance in America has worked much as life insurance, homeowners' insurance, or automobile insurance. The insured pays the insurance company a specified premium and the company guarantees some degree of protection. And like other types of insurance, health insurance premiums and benefits are figured on the basis of average experience. In order to fix rates and benefits, insurance company actuaries rely on aggregate statistics that tell them how many people in a certain population group will become ill and how much their illnesses will cost.

Here the similarity ends. Unlike life insurance or homeowners' insurance, the value of health insurance is *not* measured by the actual amount promised as a benefit—as in a $25,000, $50,000, or $100,000 life or homeowners' policy. And unlike automobile liability insurance, which fixes a limit on the amount that the company will pay, health insurance is "open-ended." That is, no one can say what the maximum benefit return on any given policy will be. Health insurance limitations often are measured *by time* (90 days, 6 months, 1 year, etc.) rather than by dollar amounts. Unlike other forms of insurance, the value of health insurance is measured according to the extent to which it reduces *potential risk* in the event of illness. That is, *how much would the patient still owe after all insurance benefits were exhausted?*

The Unpredictability of Illness or Infirmity: Average Risk vs. Potential Risk

From the individual consumer's perspective, illness or infirmity is totally unpredictable. No one can predict when illness will strike or what form it will take. Nearly everyone has friends or loved ones who have been hit out of the blue with serious illness or disability. Often the reaction is, "I never would have believed it could happen to Margaret." Conversely, most of us know people who for years think they are desperately ill, yet live on to a ripe old age. Good health, then, as well as sickness, often comes as a surprise. The belief that we can easily predict the future seems to be a persistent type of human behavior (especially among some economists who ought to know better); it must, however, be excluded from any thought regarding health insurance.

It is also crucial that *average risks* not be confused with *potential risks*. Insurance companies structure policy coverages and premium rates around the likelihood of certain conditions occurring. To be sure, a certain percentage of a specified group of people will contract a certain disease or become disabled. But this average risk experience is of little practical value to the individual.

Instead, the insurance buyer must be concerned with potential risks that seldom occur, but that everyone nevertheless faces. This point is of the utmost importance, since in their sales promotions many insurance companies cite average statistics. Far too many people have been misled by sales presentations giving general figures that frighten them into believing they will contract a certain disease or require a certain type of care. Some companies have relied almost exclusively on the power of such frightening figures to generate purchases of their policies. Again, although the averages may be accurate, they bear no relation to the potential risks to the individual arising from the unpredictability of illness.

A hypothetical case from a less emotionally charged situation will illustrate the point. Assume, for example, that more automobiles are painted white than any other color, and that *on average* white cars are involved in more accidents than any other. Would you purchase automobile insurance that protected you only in the event that a *white* automobile collided with you? Obviously not.

The unpredictability of illness and health care costs during recent decades has thrown the health insurance industry into disarray. This situation has important implications for all health insurance buyers—elderly or not. Aside from the unpredictability of illness, the costs of diagnosing and treating many conditions are uncertain. First, medical technology is rapidly altering diagnostic and therapeutic procedures for most illnesses. Sometimes the actual costs go up, and sometimes they go down. Second, illness varies from place to place and from population to population. There is no reliable way of predicting what will happen in any given area on the basis of aggregate experience. Third, and most important, health care costs vary greatly.

6

Historically, hospital and doctor fees have varied widely from place to place. Medicare administrators have attempted to regulate both hospital and physician fees, but these attempts have further complicated Medicare reimbursement procedures.

The consequences of these uncertainties—all of which are related to the unpredictability of illness—are enormous. To a greater extent than in other types of insurance, actuarial "science" in the health insurance field is unreliable.

The result has been an enormous variation in premiums and losses, and this situation has offered tremendous variation in value for the health insurance buyer. It may pay to expend considerable effort in price shopping for "medigap" insurance. In that endeavor, we hope that this booklet will be a useful resource.

II.

MEDICARE

IN order to purchase any medigap insurance policy, you must be insured under Medicare's Hospital Insurance (Part A) and Supplemental Medical Insurance (Part B). Coverage under both Medicare insurance programs has been subject to frequent change. And each time Medicare's coverage has changed, the terms of coverage of the various medigap policies then in force have also changed. Medicare administrators base their premium decisions and claims payment practices on existing legislation. But as the brief history below suggests, the Medicare laws could change again anytime. Although it may be unsettling, virtually all health insurance decisions that today's senior citizens face should be made with the understanding that they probably will be temporary ones.

Medicare's History

The Medicare program, enacted on July 30, 1965 as Title XVIII of the Social Security Act, became effective July 1, 1966. It consists of two separate parts: Hospital Insurance (Part A) and Supplemental Medical Insurance (Part B). Medicare coverage initially included only Social Security retirement beneficiaries but subsequently has undergone many changes, being extended at different times to provide coverage to disabled persons entitled to monthly cash benefits under Social Security or the Railroad Retirement program...to pay benefits for hospice care for terminally ill patients...to make Medicare the secondary payer for all workers aged 65 or older and their spouses who are covered by employment-based health insurance...to include payment for immunosuppressive drugs to transplant patients...to provide home health care benefits...and to provide coverage for mental health services.

The Medicare Catastrophic Coverage Act of 1988 greatly expanded Medicare benefits in an attempt to protect the elderly and disabled against catastrophic medical bills. This Act also provided for broad coverage of outpatient prescription drugs. The new Medicare benefits, which sparked a wave of protest from beneficiaries, were to be financed through increases in both Part A and Part B premiums.

As a result, the Medicare Catastrophic Coverage Repeal Act of

1989 rescinded the Medicare catastrophic benefits legislated the previous year and generally restored Medicare benefit levels to those available prior to January 1, 1989. The earlier legislated premium increases were canceled. An important feature of the Repeal Act holds that "Hospital and skilled-nursing facility days used in 1989 will not be counted when calculating an individual's balance of lifetime reserve days."

Initially, Medicare reimbursed healthcare providers on a fee-for-service basis. However, since 1985, Medicare payments to hospitals have been made under the "Diagnosis Related Group" (DRG) system, which in most cases pays the hospital a fixed fee according to the diagnostic group (*i.e.*, illness) for which you are admitted, no matter how long you stay or what treatment is given.

Changes have also been made in the terms of benefit payments to Medicare physicians. Under the Omnibus Budget Reconciliation Act of 1989 (OBRA), Medicare physicians are paid according to a fee schedule that was phased in over 5 years, beginning in 1992. The fee schedule is based on what Medicare authorities deem to be a "relative value scale" that pays physicians according to the number of years of training they have received, their overheads, and "geographical differences." *The Act also limits so-called excess charges, or what doctors may charge over and above the Medicare allowed fee.* This is very significant, inasmuch as doctors' charges in excess of Medicare's approved fees usually have constituted one of the largest financial risks of Medicare beneficiaries. In effect, this legislation has reduced somewhat this category of risk. More recent federal and state legislation has restricted even further what doctors can charge in excess of the Medicare allowed fee.

Most important from the point of view of this booklet, the Omnibus Budget Reconciliation Act of 1990 directed that new standards be set for Medicare supplemental insurance (medigap) policies. *According to the legislation now in force, there must be a 6-month "open enrollment" period for new beneficiaries aged 65 or older during which insurers may not deny coverage nor discriminate in the price of the policy.* That is, new Medicare subscribers now are guaranteed the availability of medigap insurance at "regular" premium prices regardless of their health history or present condition. (The insurer may make you wait for up to six months before it pays

10

benefits for preexisting conditions, but it cannot turn you down.) Moreover, under current law a medigap policy may not be canceled or a renewal refused by the insurer solely on the basis of the health of the policyholder.

Beyond this Federal legislation, the National Association of Insurance Commissioners (NAIC) developed model standards for ten Medicare Supplemental Insurance policies. According to these model standards, insurers are limited to providing policies that adhere to the coverage requirements in the ten model policies. Chapter VI discusses and Chapter VIII describes a statistical procedure for comparing the relative value of each policy.

Subsequently, the enactment of Medicare Part C (Medicare+Choice) legislation in 1997 introduced several private market-based Medicare health plan options to choose from that provide an alternative to participating in the conventional Medicare plan and to purchasing one of the ten standardized supplemental insurance policies. The options available under Medicare+Choice are discussed in Chapter IX.

Who is Eligible for Medicare?

Anyone 65 or older who is entitled to monthly benefits under the Social Security or Railroad Retirement program—or would be entitled if an application had been filed—is automatically eligible for premium-free benefits under Medicare's Hospital Insurance (Part A). Persons who are already receiving Social Security benefits will be automatically enrolled in Medicare Part A when they turn 65. Otherwise, you must enroll in Medicare by calling the Social Security Administration at 1-800-772-1213. You may also apply online at www.ssa.gov. You can receive Medicare benefits even if you continue to work. Currently, the age of eligibility for Medicare is not scheduled to rise above 65, even though the full retirement age for Social Security benefits gradually increases to 67 for those born after 1937.

A person 65 or older who is a dependent or survivor of a person entitled to Part A benefits is also eligible for these benefits. For example, a 65-year-old woman entitled to a spouse's or widow's Social Security benefit is eligible for Hospital Insurance. This is true even if her husband is only age 62–64 and has not yet applied for his Social Security benefits. However, if her husband has not yet turned

11

62, she will not qualify for Medicare when she turns 65 and must wait until her husband's 62nd birthday. Conversely, if her spouse turns 65 before she does, she does not become eligible for Medicare until her 65th birthday. In all cases the dependent spouse should contact the Social Security Administration to enroll.

In addition, several other classes of persons, some of whom must apply for coverage, are eligible for Medicare Part A, including:

- any disabled individual under age 65 entitled to monthly disability benefits for a total of 24 months (not necessarily consecutive) under Social Security or the Railroad Retirement program is automatically enrolled in Medicare Part A (spouses and children of disabled beneficiaries are *not* eligible for Medicare benefits);

- anyone under age 65 who has end-stage renal disease and who is either fully or currently insured, or is entitled to monthly benefits under the Social Security or Railroad Retirement program or is the spouse or dependent child of such an insured person or beneficiary. Eligibility begins on the first day of the third month following the month in which either dialysis terminates or the individual has a renal transplant;

- anyone under age 65 who has Lou Gehrig's Disease (ALS). Coverage begins either July 1, 2001 or the first month you get disability benefits from Social Security or the Railroad Retirement Board, whichever is later.

- anyone aged 65 or older enrolled in the Medicare Supplemental Medical Insurance program (Part B) who is not otherwise entitled to Part A benefits, upon voluntary participation with payment of a hospital insurance premium. (The full Part A premium in 2003 is $316 per month.) Persons who do not purchase Part A coverage within a specific time after becoming eligible because of age are subject to a 10-percent penalty for each 12 months they are late in enrolling. However, the 10-percent penalty will be charged against the Part A premium for only a specified time period (twice the number of years enrollment was delayed), after which the penalty will be eliminated and the premium levied as though no delay in enrollment had occurred.

Medicare's Supplemental Medical Insurance (Part B) is available to any U.S. resident, either a citizen or lawfully admitted alien with 5 years continuous residence, aged 65 or older, or any individual entitled to Medicare Part A benefits upon voluntary participation with payment of the Part B premium, which is $58.70 per month in 2003. In addition, anyone under age 65 who is entitled to Medicare Part A benefits may enroll in Part B by paying the premium. Persons who receive Social Security or Railroad Retirement benefits will be automatically covered by Part B insurance unless they indicate that they do not want it when they become eligible for Part A insurance (the premium is deducted from the Social Security benefit payment).

If you have turned 65 and want to delay your Social Security benefits, you have to apply for Medicare. If you do not enroll in Part B during your initial enrollment period but later decide you want benefits, you can sign up during the general enrollment period each year (January 1 through March 31). However, your benefits will not begin until July 1, and your monthly premium will rise by 10 percent for each 12-month period you are not enrolled in the program.

Under the Medicare+Choice program, you may opt to join a Medicare managed care plan (e.g., HMO) if you have both Part A Hospital Insurance and Part B Medical Insurance, do not have end-stage renal disease (kidney failure), and live in the service area of the plan. Although Medicare managed care plans are offered by private companies, you are still in the Medicare program. You will keep your Medicare rights and protections as well as receive the regular Medicare covered services.

To purchase a medigap insurance policy, you must be covered under both Part A and Part B of the Medicare program. You have a 6-month open-enrollment period (that begins with the first month that you are age 65 or over and also enrolled in Medicare Part B) to buy the policy of your choice. During this period, you cannot be denied coverage or charged a higher price because of current or past health problems. If you do not enroll during this period, you may not be able to get the policy you want, or you may be charged a higher premium. *You do not need to buy a medigap policy if you are in a Medicare managed care plan, or if you are covered by Medicaid.*

Current Medicare Premiums and Coverage.

Under the Medicare benefits structure now in effect, Medicare

MEDICARE BENEFITS SUMMARIZED AND PATIENT FINANCIAL RISK
HOSPITAL INSURANCE — PART A

Type of Service	Time Limit	Patient Risk	Medicare Pays	Qualifications	Exclusions
Hospital Confinement: semiprivate room and board unless a private room is required for medical reasons. Covers routine nursing, drugs, and normal services, including operating and recovery rooms, medical social services, physical therapy, equipment and medical supplies.	First 60 days each benefit period*	**First $840**	Balance	Age 65 and: (1) Entitled to Social Security (or Railroad Retirement) benefits; or (2) is *not* entitled, a citizen or permanent resident for 5 years, may enroll by paying a monthly fee plus Part B (cost below).	First three pints of blood, private duty nurses, noncovered levels of care, services covered under Part B, television, telephone and luxury items.
	Next 30 days continuous hospital confinement	**$210 each day**			
	Lifetime aggregate reserve of 60 additional days	**$420 each day**			
	After 150 days continuous hospital confinement	**100%**	Nothing		
Skilled Nursing Facilities: following hospital confinement.	First 20 days each benefit period*	**Nothing**	100% of covered charges	Must require skilled nursing or rehabilitation care within 30 days after hospital confinement that lasted at least 3 days.	Same as above; unskilled medical care (such as "Old Age Homes" and Custodial Care).
	Next 80 days continuous confinement	**$105 each day**	Balance		
	After 100 days continuous confinement each benefit period	**100%**	Nothing		
Home Health Care: by part-time visiting nurses, technicians, and therapists.	First 100 visits in spell of illness Part B covers any visits thereafter	**Nothing for covered charges; 20% of covered charges for durable medical equipment**	100% of covered services; 80% of covered amount for durable medical equipment	Must be home confined and physician must prescribe nursing/skilled care.	Full-time (private duty) nursing, homemaker services, self-administered drugs, services, covered under Part B.
Hospice Care	As long as the doctor certifies need	**Nothing†**	100% of covered services†	Must be terminally ill.	
Psychiatric Confinement Care	190-day lifetime limit		Same as Hospital Confinement with a lifetime maximum of 190 days.		
Overseas Hospital Care	No coverage	**100% of charges**	Nothing	Some coverage provided only in special circumstances.	

14

MEDICAL INSURANCE — PART B

Type of Service	Time Limit	Patient Risk	Medicare Pays	Qualifications	Exclusions
Physicians and Surgeons: services at home, hospital, or office.	No time limit	**First $100 per calendar year, then 20% of "approved charges" plus any excess of charges over Medicare's "approved charges" if doctor or supplier does not accept assignment, up to limit.**	Balance of "approved charges"	Voluntary enrollment, costs $58.70 per month plus 10% (per year) depending on date of enrollment, if you did not sign up when you were first eligible (workers and their spouses with employer group health coverage may delay enrollment and avoid the late enrollment penalty if they meet certain requirements).	Services covered by Workmens' Compensation, private duty nurses, eyeglasses, routine physicals, routine dental work, hearing aids, orthopedic shoes, nonskilled nursing care, cosmetic surgery, charges made by a relative, first three pints of blood in a calendar year, vaccinations, self-administered drugs, preventive care, services in a foreign country.
Medical Services and Supplies: diagnostic tests, surgical dressings, casts, splints, braces, artificial limbs and eyes, rental or purchase of medical equipment, ambulance, X-ray therapy, professionally administered drugs, some chiropractic services, nonroutine footcare.					
Hospital Care: Outpatient					
Home Health Care: part-time visiting nurses, aides, therapists.	Unlimited visits	**Nothing**	100% of approved charges	Same as for Part A home health care.	
Durable medical equipment.	Unlimited	**20% of costs**	80% of costs		Non-medical items.
Psychiatric Outpatient Care	Per calendar year	**First $100, 50% of "allowable charges" plus excess of charges**	You will ordinarily pay 50% of allowable charges. However, you will pay only 20% of allowable outpatient hospital charges if you would have required admission to the hospital without the treatment.		
Overseas Medical Care	No coverage	**100% of charges**	Nothing	Some coverage provided only in special circumstances in Canada and Mexico.	

* Each "benefit period" begins with the first day of hospital confinement and ends 60 days after having been discharged from a hospital or skilled nursing facility. If another hospital admission occurs after that, you must pay another deductible and the appropriate copays.

† You pay up to $5 for each prescription. Also, you pay 5% for the cost of respite care, not to exceed 5 consecutive days. There is no limit to the number of times you can get respite care.

Note: In all cases, services and supplies must be provided by Medicare-approved agencies or personnel, except in cases of emergency.

Hospital Insurance (Part A) pays most hospital costs for the first 60 days of hospitalization after a deductible amount of $840 (see the table on page 14 for a summary of current Medicare Part A benefits and premiums). After that, Medicare pays the balance of covered costs after the patient pays $210 per day for the next 30 days and $420 per day (or charges if less) for the following 60 "lifetime aggregate reserve" days. After 150 days of continuous hospitalization, Medicare Part A pays no benefits. Once the 60-day lifetime reserve has been used, it cannot be applied to subsequent illnesses. Should a new episode require hospitalization after the lifetime reserve has been expended, Medicare Part A benefits will cease after 90 days of confinement.

Medicare Part A also pays for the costs of 20 days in a skilled nursing facility after a hospitalization of at least 3 days and all but $105 per day of skilled nursing home costs for the next 80 days. After 100 days of such confinement, Medicare Part A pays nothing.

Medicare Part A helps pay for home health care and hospice care. Home health care includes part-time skilled nursing care, physical therapy, and durable medical equipment (such as wheelchairs, hospital beds, oxygen, and walkers). Hospital Insurance covers the first 100 visits following a hospital stay or a skilled-nursing facility stay. You must pay 20 percent of the approved amount for durable medical equipment.

Hospice care includes medical and support services from a Medicare-approved hospice and drugs for symptom control and pain relief. Care is generally given in your home, but short-term care in a hospice facility, hospital, or nursing home is covered when necessary. You pay up to $5 for outpatient prescription drugs and 5 percent for inpatient respite care (short-term care given to a hospice patient by another care giver so that the primary care giver can rest). To receive hospice care, patients must be certified as being terminally ill. Benefit periods include two 90-day periods, followed by an unlimited number of 60-day periods.

Medicare's voluntary Medical Insurance (Part B), which costs $58.70 per month if you enroll as soon as you are eligible, pays 80 percent of Medicare's "approved charges" for covered services after the first $100 per calendar year. In most situations, Medicare Part B does not provide coverage for outpatient prescription drugs or routine or physical examinations (unless covered as part of Medicare participating Health Maintenance Organization [HMO] services or other managed-care services under Medicare+Choice).

However, Medicare now provides for a number of preventive measures such as bone mass measurements, colorectal cancer screening, prostate cancer screening, mammogram screening, pap smear and pelvic exams, and various vaccinations. Medicare Part B home health care benefits have also been expanded to include 80 percent of the costs of durable medical equipment purchased for such care. The table on page 15 summarizes current Medicare Part B premiums and benefits. The boxes on pages 18 and 19 list specific items that are and are not covered under Medicare Part B.

How Claims are Processed and Benefits are Paid

All Medicare participants are issued a Medicare card that contains a personal claim number that must be used whenever a claim is submitted. This card is the only evidence of Medicare insurance that most providers will accept, and Medicare will not pay any claims unless a claim number is provided. (If you are in a Medicare managed care plan, your membership card will have the name of the plan on it.)

Medicare claims usually are processed by third parties that have contracted with the government. For Medicare Part A, claims are processed by insurance companies or other organizations, such as Blue Cross/Blue Shield, that are known as "intermediaries." The hospital will submit charges directly to the intermediary, and the patient will be notified of any amounts that remain due (*i.e.*, the Medicare Part A deductible and charges for uncovered services) after Medicare has paid its benefits.

Medicare Part B claims are submitted directly by the physician who treats you to a "carrier" to be processed. If the physician agrees to accept what is known as "assignment," he or she will be paid according to Medicare's "approved charges" schedule and the patient will be billed only for the Medicare coinsurance amount (*i.e.*, the 20 percent not paid by Medicare). If the physician will not accept "assignment," the doctor's office still must submit a Medicare claim to the carrier in your behalf. The patient will then be billed for the Medicare coinsurances amount *plus* any excess physician's charges up to the Medicare-allowed maximum. Current Federal law limits

MEDICARE PART B USUALLY PROVIDES COVERAGE FOR:

Physician services

Hospital outpatient services

Physical therapy, speech pathology, and occupational therapy by physicians or institutional providers

Services of independent physical and occupational therapists, subject to limits

Macular degeneration treatment using ocular photodynamic therapy with verteporfin

Diagnostic x-ray, laboratory, and other tests

X-ray, radium, and radioactive therapy

Mammography screening

Second surgical opinions

Blood transfusions after the first three pints per year

Surgical dressings, splints, casts, etc., when ordered by a doctor

Necessary ambulance services

Rental (and in some cases purchase) of durable medical equipment for home use, when prescribed by a physician

Home health services (same as Part A)

Artificial replacements

Colostomy, ileostomy, and urostomy bags and supplies

Braces for limbs, back, or neck

Mental health services

these excess charges to 15 percent above the allowed charge. Some state laws limit excess charges even further. (Assignment is discussed in more detail in Chapter III.)

Medicare also may be the "secondary payer" in certain cases where other insurance is in force. For example, if you have an automobile liability insurance policy that pays medical benefits for treatment of injuries sustained in an auto accident, a claim must be submitted to the automobile insurer and that policy's benefits must be paid before Medicare will pay any benefits. Medicare will pay the remainder of Medicare-covered charges as the "secondary payer" up to Medicare limits. Similarly, if you are employed past age 65, are enrolled in Medicare, and are also enrolled in an employer-sponsored health plan, Medicare will be the "secondary payer" with respect to Medicare-covered charges not covered by the employer-sponsored plan.

MEDICARE PART B USUALLY PROVIDES *NO COVERAGE* FOR:

Acupuncture
Chiropractic services*
Christian Science practitioners' services*
Cosmetic surgery (except after an accident)
Custodial care
Dental care*
Experimental procedures
Eyeglasses (unless related to cataract surgery)
Foot care*
Foreign health care*
Hearing aids and examinations
Homemaker services
Immunizations except for pneumonia and infection*
Injections that can be self-administered
Meals delivered to your home
Naturopaths' services
Nursing care on full-time basis at home
Orthopedic shoes*
Personal convenience items
Physical examinations that are routine
Prescription drugs and medicines taken at home*
Preventive care
Private duty nurses
Private room*
Services performed by immediate relatives
Services not reasonable and necessary
Services payable by workers' compensation
Services or items for which you are not legally obligated to pay

* May be covered under special circumstances.

Medicare also will be a "secondary payer" under such an employer-sponsored plan for a spouse age 65 or older.

Claims and payments processing are considerably different with HMOs as well as other Medicare managed-care plans, described in Chapter V.

If You Retire Before You or Your Spouse Has Reached Age 65

For most persons, Medicare eligibility begins at age 65. If you retire before that time, you should, if possible, make arrangements to continue the employer-sponsored health plan that provided coverage while you were working—or to convert that insurance to an individual policy, an option that in most instances is required by law (within specified time limits). If you retire at age 65 and become eligible for Medicare but your spouse is under age 65, current law in most states requires that group insurance carriers permit the coverage of a spouse and other dependents to be continued under the employer-sponsored plan. However, the employer has no responsibility to contribute toward the costs of such insurance and the retiree will have to pay whatever premiums are required to keep it in force.

The Politics of Medicare

In March 1999, the National Bipartisan Commission on the Future of Medicare released the final report of its two-year study. The report was immediately criticized by the Clinton Administration for not including a prescription drug benefit. President Bush resurrected the drug issue in 2002 with his proposed prescription drug benefit for Medicare. Though the Senate was unable to agree on a measure that year, the demand for consumer drug subsidies will likely grow as effective but expensive drug therapies become available for more and more clinical conditions. Although the particulars are not yet clear, a Medicare prescription drug benefit seems politically inevitable. (See the box on page 21, "A Prescription for Bankruptcy.")

It remains inescapable that Medicare, as currently administered, is unsustainable on three counts: demographics, technology, and third-party payment. In the year 2011, 77 million baby boomers (people born between 1946 and 1964) will begin flooding into the Medicare system. Over the next fifty years, the number of beneficiaries is expected to more than double while the ratio of workers to retirees is expected to decline from about 4 to 1 in the year 2000 to slightly more than 2 to 1.

In addition to the predictable deleterious effect of such population changes on Medicare's finances, new technologies and treatments that often are invoked only in the final weeks of patients' lives but that account for a substantial proportion of all outlays have greatly increased Medicare's aggregate costs during the past decade. Prolonging for even a short period the length (if not quality) of some seniors' lives has become burdensomely expensive.

Finally, numerous studies suggest that individuals will consume more, and more expensive, health care services if someone other than the consumer bears the cost. There is little reason to think that additional benefits, such as a provision for prescription drugs, would not also be subject to these same demographic, technological, and

A PRESCRIPTION FOR BANKRUPTCY

In February 2002, the National Governors Association announced that Medicaid spending had become unsustainable. Medicaid costs grew some 11 percent in 2001; meanwhile the recession cut revenues. In most state budgets, Medicaid is the largest item after education.

Prescription-drug outlays have figured significantly in the states' difficulty in paying the rising costs of Medicaid, which, unlike Medicare, already covers prescription drugs. Drug costs have risen an average of 15 percent annually since 1995, faster than overall health care costs. In addition, though only 11 percent of Medicaid beneficiaries are elderly, they account for 31 percent of outlays because their care is costly. As people age, they need more and more expensive health care, including more and newer (and hence more expensive) drug therapies.

Future entitlements threaten to do to the Federal government what Medicaid is now doing to the states—overwhelm the budget. As baby boomers age, the elderly population will soar, driving up both the number of Medicare beneficiaries and the cost of health care. Drug benefits would raise costs still higher. Medicare's trustees already have requested prompt reform to ensure the *current* Medicare system's affordability. The General Accounting Office (GAO) has warned that Medicare is "unsustainable in its present form" and that adding a drug benefit without fundamental program reform will worsen Medicare finances.

Unfortunately, whatever plan is eventually agreed upon will likely cover affordable and predictable "front-end" costs as well as the potentially huge and often unpredictable "tail-end" drug costs that pose the biggest financial risk to the elderly. Economically, there is no good reason for the government to provide "front-end" drug benefits solely on the basis of age. It does make political sense, however. Seniors seem to favor the subsidy aspect of first dollar coverage over the insurance feature of covering "tail-end" costs.

Subsidies of any sort—either to producers or consumers—tend variously to increase demand, generate scarcities, and raise costs and/or prices and outlays. If history is any indication, a prescription drug program would likely cost much more than politicians claim. (The government's lead actuary in 1965 projected that Medicare Part A would grow to $9 million by 1990; it actually cost more than $66 million.) Medicaid already covers prescription costs for poor seniors. Covering the rest through an already financially burdened Medicare program is a prescription for bankruptcy.

third-party payer factors that plague the rest of the system.

The direction of most current and proposed reforms—increasing premiums, reducing reimbursement rates, and shunting patients into managed care—does little to address Medicare's structural flaws. Rather, this direction would seem destined to compound them. As we have observed on many occasions, what seems most needed is not more regulation, but less.

III.

WHY YOU NEED "MEDIGAP" INSURANCE

FOR any illness, there will be immediate costs. You will have to visit the doctor at least once or twice. Furthermore, if the condition requires it, you will have to be hospitalized for a day or two. These initial costs, which are predictable and inevitable with most illnesses, are termed "front-end" costs by the insurance companies. They apply to the early stages of treatment, and your personal liability for them usually corresponds to your Medicare deductibles. If these were the only costs that Medicare enrollees faced, they would have little need for "medigap" insurance.

"Tail-end" costs, on the other hand, refer to those expenses that occur toward the end of an illness or remain *after* Medicare has paid all its benefits. Unlike the initial costs of an illness, the tail-end costs are virtually unpredictable. Medicare does not cover them, and if they are not protected against, they can lead to financial ruin. Extended hospital confinements can easily run into tens and often hundreds of thousands of dollars.

Many insurance policies cover both front-end and tail-end costs. But many others offer an option, for example, reduced tail-end coverage in return for front-end coverage. When presented with this option, always choose the best tail-end coverage. The later stages of hospital and medical care have the greatest financial risks. Front-end costs occur more often but they are more financially manageable. Tail-end costs are by far the largest part of the "medigap."

Any Medicare supplemental insurance policy that you purchase should, first and foremost, cover the two categories of tail-end costs that pose the greatest risk to Medicare patients: (1) the costs of catastrophic illness that may continue after Medicare Part A benefits run out and (2) the costs that remain after Medicare Part B has paid its 80 percent of "approved charges."

For many people, Medicare provides essential protection against the financial risk of health expenses. Virtually all current supplemental health plans require your participation in both Medicare programs. Therefore, until we see genuine changes in the relation between Medicare and private fee-for-service care, it is imperative that

23

you secure both Part A and Part B Medicare coverage.

The expansion of Medicare benefits described in the preceding chapter may suggest that Medicare participants are less exposed to the financial costs of hospital and medical care than they were when the Medicare program began. This is not the case. The "acid test" of any insurance program is the amount that remains after all insurance benefits have been exhausted. By this measure, the medigap (what you owe after Medicare pays its portion of your medical bills) is growing.

Many Medicare participants have complained about the high costs of prescription drugs that usually are not covered by Medicare. The median expenditure per Medicare beneficiary (without drug coverage) on prescription medication in 1999 was $617. Nationally, outpatient prescription drug spending jumped 17.3 percent in 2000, eclipsing the 6 percent rise in physician and clinical services spending. However, these costs pale in comparison with the potential financial risks of lengthy hospitalization and medical treatment.

Personal Financial Risk of Hospitalization Is Greater

The average costs of a day's stay in the hospital is now 63 times what it was in 1966 when Medicare first paid hospital benefits. At that time, the average daily cost of hospitalization was $44. By 1981, a day in the hospital cost nearly $350, and by 2000 (the most recent available data) daily hospital costs for Medicare patients averaged $2,777. Today, they almost surely are higher. As Chart 1 clearly illustrates, daily hospital charges are steadily increasing.

Even more indicative of your potential Medicare hospital liabilities is the average annual cost of hospital stays per hospitalized beneficiary. Medicare's portion of these costs in 1998 was $11,837, up from $738 in 1967—a disturbing trend when you consider that Medicare Part A benefits have not kept pace with increasing hospital charges. In 1968, Medicare Part A paid over 80 percent of all hospital charges of Medicare patients. By 1998 (again, the most recent available data), Medicare Part A benefits paid only 45 percent of covered hospital charges. Chart 2 shows this trend.

The decreasing proportion of Medicare Part A payments shown in Chart 2 probably reflects changes in both Medicare's payment system and the clinical treatment of Medicare patients. In a major "cost

24

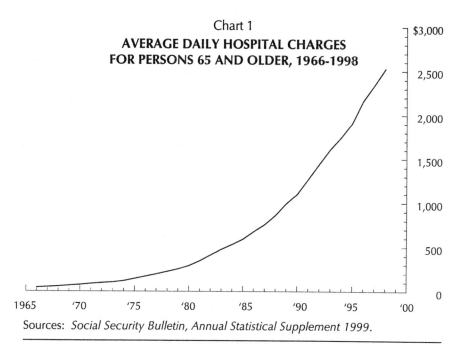

$3,000

2,500

2,000

1,500

1,000

500

0

1965   '70   '75   '80   '85   '90   '95   '00

Sources: *Social Security Bulletin, Annual Statistical Supplement 1999.*

containment" initiative, beginning in 1985, the Medicare authorities switched from fee-for-service reimbursement to the DGR (Diagnosis Related Group) system which, as described in Chapter II, pays hospitals a fixed fee according to the illness for which you are admitted, no matter how long you stay or what treatment you receive. This has reduced the portion of charges paid by Medicare. It is not clear what percentage of the unpaid charges hospitals are absorbing and what percentage passes on to Medicare patients. However, it seems unlikely that Medicare patients' liabilities have not increased in these circumstances.

Equally important, the DRG payment system has helped shorten average hospital stays, which for Medicare patients fell from over 12 days prior to 1985 to 6.0 days in 2000. Whatever this implies for the quality of patient treatment, statistically it favors a decrease in the percentage of charges paid by Medicare since shorter stays increase the portion of total expenses represented by the "front-end" Part A deductible. (It may also reflect the tendency to keep only catastrophically ill patients hospitalized for lengthy periods since those patients stay after Medicare benefits have been reduced or terminated.)

Clearly, *your personal financial risk for hospital costs is much*

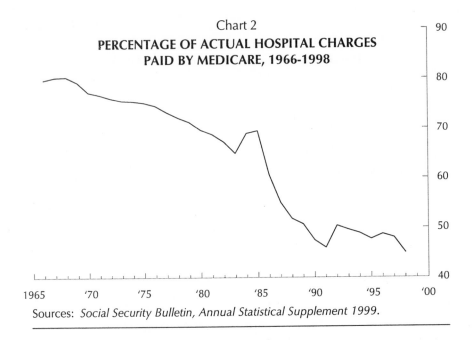

Chart 2

**PERCENTAGE OF ACTUAL HOSPITAL CHARGES
PAID BY MEDICARE, 1966-1998**

Sources: *Social Security Bulletin, Annual Statistical Supplement 1999.*

---

greater than it was only a few years ago. Even though Medicare front-end risks of hospitalization have increased from $60 in 1971 to $840 in 2003, these are manageable amounts. Tail-end risks have increased much more. In 1971, 12 months in the hospital left Medicare patients at risk for just over $20,000. By 1997, the risk of that confinement had risen over 24 times to some $500,000. Moreover, this risk accounts *only for hospital expenses.* Medical and surgical costs are additional risks. Table 1 shows how the estimated risk for different hospital stays has changed since 1971.

The Importance of "Assignment"

Assignment only applies to the services and supplies covered by Part B and only works with the "original" (fee-for-service) Medicare plan. Assignment does not apply if you are in a Medicare managed care plan (*e.g.*, HMO). *Assignment* simply means that the doctor or other health specialist who treats you agrees to accept as full payment Medicare's "approved charges." You will be responsible only for the $100 medical deductible plus additional coinsurance payments (the 20 percent of approved charges). Assignment does not mean that you have no liability, but it guarantees that a physician will not bill you for amounts beyond the Medicare approved charges.

26

Table 1
ESTIMATED FINANCIAL RISK OF HOSPITALIZATION, 1971-1997

	60 Days	90 Days	*Amount Not Paid by Medicare for:*			
			5 Months	6 Months	9 Months	12 Months
1971	$ 60	510	2,310	4,950	12,870	20,790
1972	$ 68	578	2,618	5,528	14,258	22,988
1973	$ 72	612	2,772	5,922	15,372	24,822
1974	$ 84	714	3,234	6,834	17,634	28,434
1975	$ 92	782	3,542	7,892	20,942	33,992
1976	$104	884	4,004	9,134	24,524	39,914
1977	$124	1,054	4,774	10,684	28,414	46,144
1978	$144	1,224	5,544	12,294	32,544	52,794
1979	$160	1,360	6,160	13,810	36,760	59,710
1980	$180	1,530	6,930	15,750	42,210	68,670
1981	$204	1,734	7,854	18,294	49,614	80,934
1982	$260	2,210	10,010	22,400	59,570	96,740
1983	$304	2,584	11,704	26,044	69,064	112,084
1984	$356	3,026	13,706	29,696	77,666	125,636
1985	$400	3,400	15,400	33,220	86,680	140,140
1986	$492	4,182	18,942	39,312	100,422	161,532
1987	$520	4,420	20,020	42,730	110,860	178,990
1988	$540	4,590	20,790	46,710	124,470	202,230
1990*	$592	5,032	22,792	55,852	155,032	254,212
1991	$628	5,338	24,178	62,278	176,578	290,878
1992	$652	5,542	25,102	68,482	198,622	328,762
1993	$676	5,746	26,026	74,446	219,706	364,966
1994	$696	5,916	26,796	79,356	237,036	394,716
1995	$716	6,086	27,566	84,896	256,886	428,876
1996	$736	6,256	28,336	90,869	278,468	466,066
1997	$760	6,460	29,260	97,468	302,092	506,716

* Amounts for 1989 omitted due to statistical distortion from the passage and repeal of the Medicare Catastrophic Coverage Act.

Doctors and suppliers *must* accept assignment for lab tests covered by Medicare, for Medicaid patients whose states help pay their health care costs, and for Medicare-covered drugs and biologicals billed to a Durable Medical Equipment Regional Carrier under the durable medical equipment, prosthetics, orthotics, and supplies benefit. To find physicians or suppliers in your area who accept assignment call 1-800-MEDICARE (1-800-633-4227) or TTY/TDD: 1-877-486-2048 if you are hearing or speech impaired, or search the physician and supplier directories on the internet at www.medicare.gov.

If you locate physicians who will accept assignment of fees, your financial risk can be effectively limited to the known Medicare deductible and coinsurance requirement for covered services. In these circumstances, Medicare Supplemental Insurance that restricts coverage to Medicare's coinsurance liability is adequate. You would be throwing money away by purchasing a policy that promises to pay more than 20 percent of Medicare's approved charges.

However, financial risk is the *least* of your risks in the event of life-threatening illness. You must be satisfied with the quality of health care you receive and you may not always wish to be treated by doctors who accept assignment. Top-flight specialists, for example, often charge fees that are beyond those approved by Medicare and, as discussed below, in such cases patient financial risk can be substantial. Federal law restricts doctors who do not accept assignment but who do provide services to patients who will be billed through Medicare from charging more than 15 percent above Medicare's approved charge. However, some states have even lower limits. Other specialists may not agree to any Medicare participation whatsoever, and require a private fee-for-services contract. Currently there is no limit on fee schedules agreed to under such private contracts.

For more information on assignment, call the numbers above and ask for a free copy of *Medicare & You: Does your doctor or supplier accept "assignment?"* This publication is also available at www.medicare.gov.

"Participating" Doesn't Imply Access

The Center for Medicare & Medicaid Services (formerly the Health Care Financing Administration) frequently points to the rate of "Participation" as proof that seniors have adequate access to care. This claim, however, is misleading.

Although the Medicaid's "Physician Directory" provides a listing of physicians who are "Participating," beneficiaries in some areas may find that, whereas many physicians may be listed as "Participating," few—if any—may be accepting new Medicare patients. On the other hand, many "Non-Participating" physicians may be accepting new Medicare patients.

Confusing? Probably. The term "Participating," in Medicare parlance, has nothing to do with patient access. Rather, it describes a

PUTTING PATIENTS LIVES IN DANGER

The number of hospitals losing money taking care of Medicare/Medicaid patients rose from 47 percent in 1997 to 61 percent in 1999. With government and HMO cost-containment initiatives squeezing hospital finances since the mid-90s, many RNs have been sent packing into early retirement. Others have been laid off. Those left have seen their hours and wages drop. Worse, RNs are now burdened with added patient-care responsibilities once performed by doctors. Not surprisingly, then, the Institute of Medicine reported in 1999 that some 98,000 Americans die every year from preventable medical errors made in hospitals. It would seem that patient care is bound to be affected by the nationwide shortage of hospital RNs and nurse assistants resulting from cost-saving measures.

For example, a recent survey of nurses conducted by the *American Journal of Nursing* found that more than two thirds of nurses reporting said that they don't have time to perform basic nursing care, such as teaching patients how to tend to wounds or how to inject themselves with insulin. More than half reported that they were too busy to consult with other members of the patient's health-care team. One third would not recommend that their family members receive care at the facility where they work.

Some medical analysts believe that with fewer staff doing more work, there is "imminent danger of errors of judgment and misassessment." More likely, simple schedules are apt to be confused: medication schedules may become lax, routine care or prescribed therapy may be missed, changes in patient condition may escape notice, responsibilities may be juggled, and so on. Such hospital staff errors or neglect could be harmful if not life-threatening.

None of the NAIC approved Medicare supplemental insurance policies now provides coverage for the costs of private duty nurses. Nevertheless, private duty nursing coverage would seem to be desirable, especially in instances where reference to the records of a local Peer Review Organization reveals that a medical facility has a below-average record of performance. In the current situation, the easiest way to obtain coverage of private nursing costs may be through the purchase of a hospital indemnity policy discussed in Chapter IV.

mechanism of payment. "Participating" physicians agree to accept assignment on all Medicare claims and covered services and receive their payment directly from Medicare. "Non-Participating" physicians, in contrast, can charge a slightly higher rate, but must collect their fees from the patient.

With Medicare reimbursements rates being slashed and legally capped, patients are quickly learning that "Participating" doesn't imply access.

Medical Claims Reduced

Medicare patients' average personal financial liability for physi-

---

QUICKER & SICKER?

The implementation of the prospective payment system based on DRG categories may itself pose a new "health risk" to Medicare patients. Medicare officials have become alarmed at reported instances of premature release of patients—that is, where hospitals release patients "quicker & sicker." Therefore, they now require hospitals to inform Medicare patients of their legal right to challenge their discharge from a hospital if they or their physicians believe such discharge is premature. *If the hospital does not notify you of your rights and you decide to stay after your discharge date, you can't be charged for the cost of your care.*

"Dumping" of Medicare patients whose hospital stay exceeds the DRG patient allowance for their diagnosis is a predictable result of the prospective payment system. Whether wittingly or unwittingly, hospital officials in a number of reported cases have informed their Medicare patients that their "Medicare hospital benefits have run out" and that therefore the hospital must discharge them.

Understand that *the prospective payment system does not limit your stay in the hospital to the time corresponding to the reimbursement provided by any diagnosis related group.* Your benefits cannot "run out" before your discharge is clinically warranted. As a Medicare patient, you have a right to appeal your discharge to the local medical peer review organization. That organization must issue a decision within 3 days of receiving your appeal, and the hospital cannot force you to leave before then.

cians' services and other professional services has been greater than that for hospital costs. Doctors' bills have accounted for the largest part of private liabilities by a wide margin. Even after Medicare Part B has paid its benefits, doctors' bills have remained a large financial risk for most Medicare subscribers. This is because Medicare will pay only its "allowed charges," not what a doctor may actually charge. In 2003, Medicare pays 80 percent of *allowable charges* after the $100 deductible has been paid by the patient. However, patient risk may still be great since a doctor may charge as much as 15 percent more than allowable charges.

Most people entering the Medicare program probably expect that

---

If your appeal is granted, you may stay in the hospital and it must absorb any cost of your treatment that exceeds the DRG reimbursement amount.

If your appeal is denied, you still cannot be charged for the days of your hospitalization that follow the hospital's notification of its intent to discharge you and prior to the peer review organization's decision, which should be no more than 3 days.

Although one would expect that in most cases of attempted premature discharge, your attending physician would offer full support of any warranted appeal you may make (or actually initiate it), be aware that the prospective payment system has imposed disincentives to such appeals by physicians: even if a doctor follows the guidelines set by a peer review panel to admit or retain a patient, the same panel can later disallow the stay and reimbursement. Peer review panels are primarily engaged in slashing expenses, and any physician who interferes with a review organization's task of cutting costs risks being labeled a "Medicare abuser" and losing hospital privileges.

Thus, it is your responsibility to initiate the appeal process if, after consultation with your physician, you feel that you are being discharged prematurely.

When you are admitted to a Medicare participating hospital, you should be given a copy of *An Important Message From Medicare*. It explains your rights as a hospital patient. If you are not given one, ask for it. The message explains what to do if you think the hospital is making you leave too soon. If you have questions about this, call the Quality Improvement Organization (QIO). Their number is on the message.

Part B insurance will pay a good portion of their physician, outpatient hospital, and home health services. This is not necessarily the case. In 2000, for instance, Medicare Part B reimbursed *only* 58.6 percent of *allowed* charges for all covered services billed for persons aged 65 or older. The other two-fifths, which were not reimbursed, is in addition to patient liabilities for uncovered charges.

Medicare's "Allowable Charge"

These data on claim reductions reveal the capriciousness of Medicare's "allowable charge" determination procedure. That procedure effectively leaves you at the greatest possible risk within the terms of coverage.

Three different figures are used to arrive at the "allowable charge": (1) the customary charge, (2) the prevailing charge, and (3) the actual charge. As defined by Medicare, the *customary charge* is "generally the charge most frequently made by each doctor and supplier for each separate service or supply furnished to patients in the previous calendar year." The *prevailing charge* is "the amount which is high enough to cover the customary charges in three out of every four bills submitted in the previous year for each service and supply." The *actual charge* is what you are billed by the doctor or hospital. When a claim reaches Medicare, the "approved charge" is the lowest of these three amounts. In practice, the actual charge is almost never the lowest.

Medicare Does Not Travel Abroad

If you travel out of the country during your retirement years, you should arrange for payment of hospital and medical care in the event of illness. Except in three very restrictive situations, Medicare covers neither hospital costs nor medical costs abroad.

The special circumstances under which Medicare might provide coverage are:

1. You are in the United States when an emergency occurs and the closest hospital available to treat you is in Mexico or Canada. For example, if you are traveling close to either border and become ill, you are covered for care in a Mexican or Canadian hospital if it were the closest hospital to handle your emergency.

2. Your home in the United States is closer to a Canadian or

Mexican hospital than a U.S. hospital. In this case, you are covered for both emergency and non-emergency care.

3. You are traveling from Alaska by the most direct route to another state. Medicare will cover emergency medical costs for treatment in Canada.

Most but not all Medicare supplemental policies provide coverage for emergency health care in foreign countries.

Other Uncovered Services

As the list on page 19 suggests, Medicare still does not cover many other health care services—and some of these may be costly. Of particular concern is the risk that current "cost containment" measures may pose to the quality of care you receive in a hospital. Many physicians now recommend that you acquire the services of a private duty nurse if you are hospitalized (see box, "Putting Patients Lives in Danger" on page 29).

In short, there is a "medigap" that requires supplementary insurance to pay benefits in excess of Medicare's reimbursement schedule and to protect you against possible neglect or abuse by cost-conscious administrators and harried health workers (see box, "Quicker & Sicker" on pages 30 and 31).

Part 2 of this book discusses currently available "medigap" insurance options. These options are, of course, subject to change at any time if the politicians decide to tinker further with the Medicare program.

Part 2

HOW TO PROTECT YOURSELF AGAINST THE "MEDIGAP"

IV.

ALTERNATIVES TO HEALTH INSURANCE POLICIES

FOR a number of years, many health-related insurance policies have aimed at the Medicare market. This is understandable. For the past 50 years, the retired have had the most reliable incomes of any segment of the population. Although small in relation to their working-years' incomes, the more-or-less guaranteed aspect of retirement income, combined with the health consequences of aging, generated a great deal of market interest within the insurance industry.

One result of this interest has been the proliferation of limited-coverage health policies. These have relatively low premiums and are affordable to most retired persons. However, they cover only a small portion of the potential health risk of the elderly. These policies isolate a particular disease or situation, and their sales approach generally exploits the understandable fears of most of us. Limited-coverage policies are not the bargains they appear to be and are no substitute for comprehensive insurance.

In general, any policy that limits coverage to a particular set of conditions violates the health insurance principle, which is to reduce potential risk regardless of the circumstances of illness. All states allow the sale of limited policies in one form or another. But Federal law prohibits their sale as "supplemental health insurance." Limited policies such as accident, "dread disease" or cancer, and daily indemnity insurance leave wide gaps in coverage and thus in financial risk. Their traditional popularity testifies powerfully to the persistence of the myths surrounding elderly health risks. For the most part, these policies create only the illusion of greater protection.

Accident Insurance

Accident insurance is *not* health insurance. These policies pay hospital and medical costs only if you have been injured as a result of accident. They frequently impose limits on benefits that are far below actual costs of rehabilitation.

Accident indemnity policies, which promise to pay a specified amount for the loss of one or both eyes, arms, or legs in an accident, are so narrowly written that they apply only in an infinitesimally small set of circumstances. Amputees who have had their limbs removed for clinical reasons, for example, are not protected by such policies. *Accident insurance is a waste of money.*

"Dread Disease" and Cancer Policies

These policies, which usually are solicited either through the mail, in newspapers and magazines, or by salesmen working on commission, are notoriously poor values. They appeal to unrealistic fears, cover only very specific conditions, and cannot substitute for comprehensive insurance. Consequently, some states have prohibited their sale.

Even if you contract an insured disease, you will not likely be hospitalized long enough to receive the benefits that would justify the premiums on these policies. Moreover, special disease policies normally do not provide protection against many types of costs incurred as a result of the disease, such as home care, transportation, and rehabilitation.

Most cancer policies contain one or more of the following limiting conditions:

- Some pay only if you are hospitalized. Today, most cancer care, such as radiation treatment and chemotherapy, is provided on an outpatient basis. The average hospital stay for cancer patients was only 7 days in 1999.

- No policy will provide protection against cancer diagnosed before you applied for the policy.

- Most cancer insurance does not cover related illnesses, such as infection, diabetes, or pneumonia.

- These policies often require waiting periods of anywhere from 30 days to several months before coverage becomes effective. Many stop paying benefits after a fixed period of 24 or 36 months.

- Although a number of these policies increase coverage after 90 consecutive days in the hospital, this feature is nearly worthless since 99 percent of all cancer patients spend fewer than 60 days in the hospital.

Cancer policies have traditionally posted the lowest loss ratios (the percentage of premiums that are returned to policyholders as benefits)—sometimes only 20 percent—of all forms of health insurance. As with accident indemnity policies, *special disease insurance is a waste of money.*

Hospital Indemnity Policies

Hospital indemnity policies that promise to pay you a fixed amount for each day you spend in the hospital have been widely advertised on television. Actors hired for their high "trust quotients" counsel elderly viewers in soothing yet urgent tones to subscribe to their particular plan, which is often made to sound exclusive. In fact, indemnity policies that usually promise to pay between $50 and $100 a day are not health insurance. Although they may be useful in some circumstances, as discussed below, *the average benefit return does not justify the premium cost of this kind of policy.*

When an Indemnity Policy May Be Useful

Indemnity policies may have value under some conditions. Advertisements describe them as supplemental income plans; the law prohibits them from being advertised as otherwise. If you already have supplemental insurance, an indemnity policy may be attractive as a source of income in the event of extended hospitalization. This type of benefit can help to defray associated expenses, such as transportation and home maintenance, that may not otherwise be covered by health insurance.

Many people buy indemnity policies hoping they will "make money" if they get sick. Purchased this way, an indemnity policy is merely a gamble similar to buying a lottery ticket. If your potential risk does not justify the policy—either because it is too high or too low—you are throwing your money away.

Whether or not an indemnity policy is worthwhile depends on two separate considerations. First, to what extent will hospitalization place you at financial risk for nonmedical reasons? Second, to what extent will the policy reduce this financial risk?

Everyone incurs some nonmedical expense as a result of hospital confinement. If nothing else, the lawn has to be mowed and household chores have to be done. The important question is: Can these routine expenses be handled out of pocket, or does your situation

39

involve financial risk that merits the purchase of separate income insurance? For example, would you have to hire full-time help to maintain your residence while you were in the hospital? Would you suffer a loss of essential income? Would others be deprived of your needed services because of your absence (if, say, your spouse or another household member relies on you for daily care)? Do you conduct a business that would require you to employ someone if you were in the hospital? In short, the extent of your nonmedical risk determines if you should consider an indemnity policy. This assumes that you can afford its premium costs over and above the price of supplemental health insurance. *You should not sacrifice supplemental health insurance coverage in order to pay premiums on a hospital indemnity policy.*

As a rule of thumb, a hospital indemnity policy may be justified only if it reduces your nonmedical potential risk by between 50 percent and 150 percent. If it reduces your risk by less than 50 percent, you need some other form of protection. If it pays you more than 150 percent of your anticipated risk, you are better off to absorb the risk.

In addition, a hospital indemnity policy might now be useful for one medical reason. The new medigap policies (described in Chapter VI) no longer cover private duty nursing costs. Inasmuch as many physicians now advise that a private duty nurse is highly desirable in many clinical situations, a hospital indemnity policy may be a useful way of covering all or a part of such expense. Some *existing* medigap policies continue to provide coverage for private duty nursing—and holders of those policies might be well-advised to retain them.

To find the best value in indemnity policies, calculate a benefit-cost index by dividing the benefit for the first 30 days of hospitalization by the monthly premium. The higher the index figure, the better the value.

Which is the better value?

Policy A pays $75 per day after the first 3 days of hospitalization and costs $6.52 per month.

Policy B pays $60 per day as soon as you enter the hospital and costs $5.89 per month.

Policy A: 27 x 75 ÷ 6.52 = 310.58

Policy B: 30 x 60 ÷ 5.89 = 305.60

The index for Policy A is higher; therefore, Policy A represents the better value.

Health Associations

Health associations (not to be confused with Health Maintenance Organizations, discussed in Chapter V) usually are local organizations designed to provide routine and emergency health care more conveniently in relatively isolated areas. They usually operate one or more clinics and employ a small number of physicians, dentists, and supporting staff.

For a nominal fee of $20 to $40 per year, anyone can join the association. Membership entitles you to participation in the association's programs and allows you to make appointments with doctors and dentists at the association's clinics.

Health associations provide no health insurance. You are responsible for any charges. You must have your own insurance.

Employer Insurance and Self-Insurance

Many employers participate in group health insurance programs offered by various insurance companies. These group employee plans often give the best value available in health insurance to employees, and many—though not all—are convertible to Medicare supplemental plans after retirement. If your employer offers a health insurance plan, you should contact the personnel or benefits office to determine what kind of protection is available to you after retirement. *As a rule, employer-obtained group insurance offers a far better value than individual policies,* but not always. You must compare with other forms of health coverage, such as Health Maintenance Organizations that are discussed in Chapter V.

Employer health benefits for retirees are expected to erode over the coming years according to a 2002 report by the human resources consulting firm Watson Wyatt Worldwide. Increasing health-care costs are making the cutbacks necessary for large employers who now generally pay over half of total retiree medical expenses. By 2031, these companies are expected to pay less than 10 percent of these same expenses. Although most of the changes will likely be borne by current employees and especially new hires, retirees should be prepared for possible disruption or termination of their employer group insurance coverage.

If your employer plan ends, federal law gives you the right to buy either Medigap Plan A, B, C, or F (described fully in Chapter VI) within 63 days of the date you lose your group coverage, provided the Medigap Plan is offered in your state. The insurance company cannot deny you the policy, place conditions on the policy such as a waiting period, apply a preexisting condition exclusion, or discriminate in the price of the policy based on your health status. Make sure you keep a copy of your plan's termination letter. (Some states provide more medigap protection than federal law.)

A small percentage of employers now offer their employees health plans that are totally independent of the insurance industry. Termed "self-insurance," the employer assumes some or all of the risk of the health plan. Instead of paying premiums to an insurance company, the employer pays claims from its own funds and contracts independently with physicians and hospitals to provide health care to its employees. In a few instances, such as the Kaiser complex in California, employers have constructed their own hospital facilities. Self-funding gives employees greater flexibility and control of their health benefits plan.

Contracts with employers are particularly inviting to Health Maintenance Organizations and Preferred Provider Organizations. In this instance, costs are kept down and benefits often are greater than other arrangements provide. This type of "self-insurance" has become increasingly popular with employers with access to Health Maintenance Organizations and Preferred Provider Organizations.

V.

MEDICARE+CHOICE

IN an attempt to enlarge the choices to Medicare beneficiaries, the Balanced Budget Act of 1997 expanded Medicare with the creation of a parallel program called Medicare+Choice (M+C). Under M+C, Medicare participants with both Part A and Part B coverage may choose, subject to availability, among a variety of private market-based health care plans similar to those available to the non-Medicare population.

Medicare beneficiaries may still opt for just the original fee-for-service plan run by the Federal Government. You pay the $58.70 Part B premium (in 2003), Part A and Part B deductibles, and any fees for services not fully covered by Medicare. You have access to any doctor that accepts Medicare and you receive the basic Part A and Part B services discussed in Chapter II.

As explained in Chapter III, the original fee-for-service plan entails significant financial risks because Medicare does not cover many medical expenses. Medigap insurance, discussed in Chapter VI, is one way to protect yourself against these risks. Medicare+Choice was also intended to reduce those risks. (*You do not need to buy a medigap policy if you are in an M+C plan or if you are covered by Medicaid.*)

M+C options include several managed-care arrangements—health maintenance organizations (HMOs), HMOs with point of service (POS) options, provider sponsored organizations (PSOs), preferred provider organizations (PPOs)—and nonmanaged-care, private fee-for-service (PFFS) plans. The 1997 law also authorized medical savings accounts (MSAs) and allows providers to privately contract for services with Medicare beneficiaries given certain restrictions.

HMOs (including HMOs with POS options) began serving Medicare beneficiaries in 1982, predating the M+C program by 15 years. In 2001, more than 5.5 million beneficiaries were enrolled in 179 HMOs across the country.

Like all managed-care plans, HMOs in theory provide health care more efficiently than conventional fee-for-service arrangements. Under what is now called the "original Medicare plan," Medicare pays doctors and other health care providers directly for each service a patient receives. Under managed care health plans, however, Medicare pays a lump sum, called the *capitation rate*, to the plan administrator who in turn manages the services you receive. The administrator contracts directly with hospitals and other health-care providers, paying them a predetermined amount based on the number of patients they serve and the types of services they provide, rather than a fee based on the actual costs of providing these services. If the providers' costs exceed the predetermined payment, they lose money. Thus, participating hospitals and doctors have greater incentives to keep costs down.

Therefore, under managed care, your out-of-pocket costs (premiums and copays) are usually lower. Moreover, beneficiaries do not have to contend with burdensome paperwork or the irregularities of Medicare's "approved charges" schedule. HMOs have no preexisting illness clauses, waiting periods, or elimination periods. Members are entitled to full coverage as soon as they enroll.

HMOs generally provide better coverage than conventional fee-for-service arrangements. Federally certified HMOs must offer all services covered by Medicare and must meet minimum protection standards prescribed for supplemental health insurance policies. Although most HMOs currently offer plans that pay for physical examinations, office visits, immunizations, routine eye examinations, hearing aid examinations, and dental care, some of the lower cost "basic" packages have begun dropping eye, hearing, and dental coverage.

The percentage of Medicare beneficiaries with access to zero-premium M+C plans declined dramatically from 61 percent in 1999 to 32 percent in 2002. Zero-premium M+C plans have no premium charge (beyond the Medicare Part B premiums) for beneficiaries who wish to enroll. Moreover, during that period, the percent of Medicare patients with access to a M+C plan with drug coverage also declined, from 65 percent to 50 percent.

Beware, then, that your choice of HMO plan will affect your costs, what extra benefits you receive, and how much choice you have among doctors, specialists, and hospitals (quality and access). And beware that any plan's benefits and costs are subject to change from year to year, and that Medicare health plans are free to terminate their contract with Medicare at the end of each calendar year. *HMO withdrawals from the M+C program have affected over 2 million Medicare beneficiaries since 1998.*

HMOs with a Point of Service (POS) option, originally called "open-ended HMOs," have been around since 1961. Members can choose to use the HMO network or to go outside the network each time they need care. If they choose to use the network, their primary-care physicians coordinate the care.

From a purely financial standpoint, it is always in the member's best interest to use the network. However, from a health care stand-point, it may make sense to go outside the network for certain care. With the POS option, members can go to the provider of choice *without coordination or approval* of the primary care physician or so-called gatekeeper. Claims for out-of-network care, usually much larger than in-network copays, are reimbursed after any applicable deductible and coinsurance provisions are met. Furthermore, non-network providers may charge much more than the network's reimbursement levels.

POS plans are best suited for people who would generally stay within the HMO network for most of their routine care but value the freedom to go out-of-network if a major illness strikes. In essence, the POS option acts as a (costly) safety valve.

Other Managed-Care Options

The roots of **Preferred Provider Organizations (PPOs)** can be traced back to the early 1930s and today a majority of Americans under age 65 are enrolled in one. PPOs consist of hospitals and physicians who agree to provide services at negotiated fees. Third-party payers, such as insurance companies or large employers, can access the network to provide health care services for covered individuals. The PPO charges an access fee that varies with the services used and does not generally require members to choose a primary-care doctor or remain in-network as do HMOs.

Like HMO plans with POS option, PPOs are best suited to people who plan to stay "in-network" for most their health care services but who do not want to be permanently "locked-in" to a particular doctor or hospital or who do not always want to obtain permission from a primary care physician to see a specialist.

Beginning in 2003, Medicare will test 33 PPOs that will serve seniors in 23 states. These plans will include prescription drug coverage. Enrollments start November 15, 2002, and the test is scheduled to run for three years with contracts renewable annually. A major risk of this "test" would seem to be the potential for disruptions to enrollees' services and network of providers in the event the test fails. Contact Medicare at 1-800-MEDICARE or online at www.medicare.gov for more information for your area.

Provider-Sponsored Organizations (PSOs), as the name suggests, consist of doctors and hospitals that have formed their own plans. The providers themselves, not insurance companies, run the plan. These organizations are relatively new and untested. An important question is how large the network of participating doctors is in a particular plan. While some metropolitan-area PSOs have grown into large conglomerates of providers offering extensive services, PSO care-giver networks are often more limited than either HMOs or PPOs. It would seem crucial in such cases that enrollees be permitted to seek treatment outside the PSO in a manner similar to PPOs and HMOs with POS option. If not, patient choice could be severely limited.

Information on Options Available in Your Area

You can compare the premiums and benefits of the Medicare health plans available in your area by visiting www.medicare.gov and using the "Medicare Health Plan Compare" search tool. Just type in your zip code or click on your state to call up the plans in your area. After selecting the plans you wish to compare, choose the "Costs and Benefits Report" section. Those without internet access at home or through a friend may find it worthwhile to visit their local library, community college, or senior center and ask for assistance in getting on the website. You can also call Medicare for information on the Medicare health plans in your area.

FOR MEDICARE INFORMATION

Call 24 hours a day, including weekends
1-800-MEDICARE (1-800-633-4227)
TTY 1-877-486-2048
Visit www.medicare.gov

The "Cost and Benefits" section allows you to compare the original Medicare plan and M+C plans available in your service area in three ways: (1) "Basic Information"—a side-by-side comparison of basic plan information such as premium, doctor and hospital choice, prescription drug benefits, and extra benefits; (2) "Detailed Information" for each plan covering 36 categories of benefits; and (3) "One Service"—a side-by-side comparison of all plans sccording to a feature you select (*e.g.*, prescription drugs).

If you are mainly interested in a plan for its prescription drug benefit, understand that coverage caps, co-payments, and how the price of a drug is applied to the cap (ask the plan) will affect the value of the benefit. To determine the value of the drug benefit, first total your drug costs for the year, and then subtract the sum of the following items: the plan's co-payments, the uncovered cost (cost after co-payments less cap), and the annual plan premium. The larger this difference, the greater the benefit of the drug coverage. Note that owing to the rising cost of pharmaceuticals, many plans are raising premiums, raising co-payments, lowering caps, only paying for drugs on an approved list (called the formulary), or some combination thereof.

Disadvantages of HMOs

A major disadvantage of HMOs is that members are generally limited to care under participating physicians and hospitals. (As with all managed-care options, you must reside in the plan's service area.) Many plans claim they have a large pool of member physicians, and often their prospectuses list all physicians who participate in their program. By implication, HMO members are free to choose their care providers from a large number of clinical personnel. In practice, the number of participating doctors may be deceptive. Very often, the most sought-after physicians already are "fully subscribed." Hence, even though the total number of physicians in the HMO may be quite large, the proportionately few who may accept *new* patients may be the relatively inexperienced practitioners.

Before you join an HMO, you should determine which HMO physicians are available to *new* members. If you are not satisfied with that list of doctors, you should go elsewhere.

If you become dissatisfied with your doctor, you can change to another within the organization. But you still are limited to care under HMO physicians who are accepting new patients. This rule does not apply if you require a specialist who is not in the plan. In this case, HMO physicians will refer you to several specialists, and the HMO may pay the costs of whomever you select. If an illness requires major surgery, it normally must be performed in an HMO-participating hospital. You are free to choose your own surgeon, but if you elect to have surgery performed elsewhere, you likely will have to pay the entire bill yourself unless you have a POS option.

To date, there have been relatively few studies published on HMO quality-of-care. In the past, the cost-cutting measures of managed care have reportedly led to numerous abuses and inconveniences for members: long waiting times for appointments, tests, and treatment; repeated shifting of patient assignments (you may not see the same doctor from one visit to the next); lack of concern for patient welfare; and reluctance to proceed with high-cost treatment or referrals to specialists outside the plan even when it is clinically warranted.

Most patients indicate overall satisfaction with the care they receive. Large majorities of beneficiaries report visiting their usual doctor, and of those, 95 percent say they were either satisfied or very satisfied with their care. Those with a usual place of care, but not a usual doctor, were less satisfied. However, 85 percent of these patients reported being either satisfied or very satisfied with their care. At the same time, it is interesting that *voluntary* disenrollments from M+C plans have been rising along with involuntary disenrollments, and that almost half of those leaving on their own are exiting managed care altogether and returning to traditional Medicare.

At bottom, you should carefully investigate the plans you are thinking of joining. Check the credentials of any doctor you are considering as a "primary care provider." In many states, the state medical board will tell you if a doctor is licensed, has been sued for malpractice, has been disciplined, or has received complaints. Ask friends and neighbors about the HMO physicians. Call or visit the doctors you are most interested in and ask the questions that are most important to you. For example, will they advise you over the phone on common medical problems? Do they treat other patients with your problem?

Find out as much as you can about participating hospitals—all hospitals are not created equal. How well does the staff treat people with your condition? (Providers are more successful the more they perform a procedure.) Do many patients get infections? Talk to plan members. Are they satisfied with the care they have been getting? Have their complaints been addressed? Would they join the HMO now, given their knowledge of its operations?

For many helpful contacts and suggestions on selecting physicians and hospitals, call Medicare and ask for copies of "Choosing a Doctor" and "Choosing a Hospital." These guides were developed jointly by Medicare and the Agency for Healthcare Research and Quality. You may also download them from Medicare's website.

You can also obtain information about the quality of plans in your area from Medicare's website using the "Medicare Health Plan Compare" search tool. First, type in your zip code or click on your state to call up the plans in your area. Then choose "Quality." The data, which have been carefully checked for accuracy by Medicare, have been collected both from the managed care plans themselves and directly from the beneficiaries enrolled in the plans. Currently, the information has been updated through the year 2001. Here is a sampling of the statistics you will find (given in percentages on the website):

- Members who said they always got care when they needed it without long waits

- Those who rated their own care as the best possible

- Members who said the plan doctors always communicate well

- Beneficiaries who did not have problems getting referred to a specialist

- Providers who stayed in the plan for at least one year

- Members who left over the quality of health care

As a rule of thumb, when measuring quality, a difference of ten percentage points between plans' scores on a particular measure indicates a significant difference.

The "Medicare Health Plan Compare" search tool on Medicare's website also provides reasons plan members left their plan in 2000. The reasons members leave are divided into two categories: "Health Care or Services" and "Costs and Benefits." Each category is further broken down into subcategories.

If you have determined that the quality of medical services provided by the HMO meets your criteria, you still must be concerned about its financial health. Mismanagement has landed a number of plans in financial difficulty. Medicare regulations require that defunct HMOs continue to provide coverage for Medicare subscribers for six months after bankruptcy is declared, after which time your coverage ends, potentially disrupting your medical care.

While the government protects you somewhat in case you lose your M+C coverage due to no fault of your own (see "Losing Your M+C Coverage," discussed below), *there can be no guarantee that your doctor participates in any of the alternative Medicare programs, including the original program.* Citing insufficient payments from the government, increasing numbers of doctors are dropping Medicare patients or refusing to accept new ones.

As many as two-thirds of the country's HMOs have at times operated in the red, and many of these could be sold or merged with other organizations. Therefore, try to determine the financial status of an HMO before joining. In addition to requesting a copy of the plan's most recent financial statement, you should ask a plan representative:

- How many of the HMO's physicians have left during the past five years? If there has been a "mass exodus" of doctors, you want to know why. Try to interview any such physicians.

- Is it an independent financial entity or part of a larger organization (HMO chain)? If it is part of a larger chain, ask to see the annual report of the parent group.

- Is it owned by an insurance company? If so, check that company's financial statements. If the HMO is taking losses, the company may try to sell or dismantle it.

- Is the Medicare segment of the HMO reporting losses? If so, are there plans to cancel membership for Medicare recipients?

How to Double-Check an HMO's Financial Status

If HMO representatives are reluctant to answer your questions or do not provide you with the materials you request, do not do further business with them. If they provide answers, you still should "double check" the accuracy of their statements.

Best's *Managed Care Reports-HMO*, Standard and Poor's, and Weiss Ratings now provide financial reports and ratings for HMOs. These may be available in the reference section of your local library. Rating agencies are also available by phone or online: A.M. Best Company, (908) 439-2200, www.ambest.com; and Standard & Poor's, (212) 438-2400, www.standardandpoors.com. Other HMO "chains" are listed in the *Value Line Investment Survey*, a regularly updated survey that ranks the safety and financial performance of publicly traded stocks.

Weiss Ratings rates the financial status of over 1,700 health-insurance companies, including over 700 HMOs and all the Blue Cross, Blue Shield plans. Ratings cost $15 each, or you can get a state-by-state list of all top-rated HMOs and insurers for $35. For more information, call (800) 289-9222 or visit www.weissratings.com.

It is only common sense that Medicare recipients avoid any HMO that is likely to be liquidated or to cancel Medicare memberships. However, if you find an HMO that is well-established, financially strong, and clinically superior, membership may provide good value relative to that of conventional medigap insurance. Otherwise, it would seem prudent to forgo such membership until a more financially solid HMO becomes available.

Losing Your M+C Coverage?

If your M+C coverage terminates for one of the following reasons, you have the right to return to the original Medicare plan and purchase supplemental (medigap) insurance as described:

- If, when you first became eligible for Medicare at age 65, you enrolled in an M+C plan and then disenrolled from that plan within 12 months of the effective date of your enrollment, you have the right to purchase, within 63 calendar days, *any* medigap policy sold in your state.

- If you join an M+C plan after you first become eligible for Medicare, drop your medigap policy, and subsequently disenroll from the M+C plan within the first year, you may return to your original policy if it is still available from the same insurance company, provided this was the first time you joined an M+C plan. Otherwise, you may purchase medigap policies A, B, C, or F (discussed in Chapter VI) if sold in your state. In either case, you must apply for your policy within 63 calendar days after your M+C plan ends.

- If your M+C plan coverage ends because (1) your plan terminated its Medicare participation or stopped providing care in your area, (2) you moved outside the plan's service area, or (3) you left the plan because it failed to meet its contractual obligations, you have the right to purchase medigap policies A, B, C, or F that are sold in your state. You must apply for medigap within 63 calendar days of losing your coverage.

In each of the above cases, the insurance company cannot deny you the policy, place conditions on the policy such as a waiting period, apply a preexisting condition exclusion, or discriminate in the price of the policy based on your health status. (Make sure you keep a copy of your plan's termination letter to prove that you lost coverage in a situation described above.)

Otherwise, should you *voluntarily* disenroll from an M+C plan *one year or more after joining* and decide to return to the original Medicare plan and wish to purchase a medigap policy, you risk being subjected to medical underwriting standards. *The insurance company may deny your application or impose policy restrictions and charge you more because your health is unacceptable.* This is very important. Once you are enrolled in M+C for more than a year, you may find it difficult or costly—if not impossible—to get a medigap policy should you then decide to disenroll from M+C.

With the steady stream of managed-care plans flowing out of Medicare since the inception of Medicare+Choice and the remaining plans watering down benefits, these "guarantees" provide an important safety net for your medical coverage. However, as already explained, you must still be prepared for potential disruption of your health care, especially if your doctor or hospital does not participate in one of your alternative options or if the coverage you desire is not included in any of the "guaranteed" plans.

If you are fortunate enough to live in an area with one or several M+C options, you may take advantage of another government guarantee: Under legislation signed by President Bush in June 2002, until 2005 you can enroll in any of the managed plans or private fee-for-service plans in your area at any time—provided the plan is accepting new members. In addition, *all* M+C plans must be open to new members between November 15 and December 31. It does not matter how long you have been in Medicare or how long you have been in your current plan, if you have one. This legislation only applies if you are moving *into* M+C from the original Medicare plan or from a medigap plan, or if you are moving *within* M+C from plan to plan. The June 2002 legislation does not apply to beneficiaries *leaving* M+C and returning to (or entering) the medigap market. In this case, the original guarantees, detailed above, apply. (You may elect to disenroll at any time and for any reason from most Medicare health plans. Simply write or call your plan, or call Medicare.)

The HMO/Medicare Outlook

The Balanced Budget Act of 1997 (BBA 1997) not only expanded the types of plans that may contract with Medicare, but it also changed the way they are paid. Prior to the act, Medicare paid HMOs 95 percent of what the government would have paid had enrollees remained in traditional Medicare. The new capitation rate set by BBA 1997 is the highest of three amounts: (1) a blend of local and national rates, (2) a single "floor rate" set in 1998 and increased in 2001, (3) a two percent increase from the previous year's rate.

The new formulas were designed to increase payments to rural areas where there are few Medicare HMOs, thereby reducing geographic variation and leading supposedly to a greater penetration of Medicare managed care across the country. Consequently, annual payment increases in many urban areas have averaged only 2 percent, and most HMOs are having increasing difficulty contracting with providers, whose costs are rising faster than Medicare's capitation rates. Many of these managed-care plans have been forced to reduce benefits, increase premiums, or leave Medicare.

Medicare HMOs have been confined mostly to cities and suburbs where the higher population densities of both seniors and providers make managed care viable. In effect, then, BBA 1997, by shifting the financial incentives for HMOs from urban to rural areas where demographics are unfavorable, has put a serious financial squeeze on almost the entire Medicare managed-care program. In addition, the unpredictability of payments and unstable and burdensome regulations have also contributed to the problems of M+C.

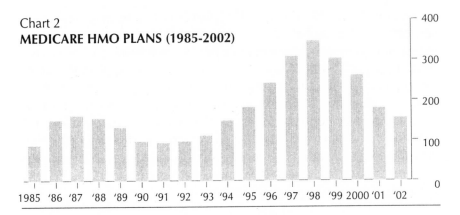

Chart 2
MEDICARE HMO PLANS (1985-2002)

Prior to BBA 1997, enrollment in Medicare managed-care plans rose steadily from 440,000 in 1985 to 1.8 million in 1993 to the peak of 6.3 million in 1999. However, since the inception of M+C, HMO participation in Medicare has fallen dramatically from a high of 346 plans in 1998 to 155 plans in 2002—sharply reversing the seven-year run-up that began in 1991 (see Chart 2). During the five years 1998 through 2002 inclusive, a total of 2.2 million Medicare beneficiaries lost HMO coverage due to plan withdrawals. In 2001 alone, withdrawals affected almost a million persons, or 14.7 percent of M+C enrollees. A nationwide survey of more than a thousand HMOs released in September 2002 by the American Association of Health Plans indicates that at least 200,000 more beneficiaries will lose their Medicare HMO coverage in 2003. Clearly, *seniors cannot count on these plans.*

As explained earlier, the surviving plans are raising premiums and cutting benefits. Even so, managed-care benefits, which often include routine office visits, preventive care, and routine eye exams, are still, on average, more extensive than fee-for-service benefits. Out-of-pocket costs (premiums and copays) are usually lower as well. However, all of this comes at the price of confining your care to the HMO's provider network. These networks are currently being pressured by disgruntled doctors and hospitals whose reimbursements have not kept pace with costs. Consequently, some providers are leaving these networks.

If you live in a rural county, you may be spared the problem of losing your Medicare HMO coverage since you will likely have no choice to begin with. While four in ten beneficiaries nationwide had no managed-plan choice in 2002, of those living in "rural areas adjacent to urban areas," about 78 percent had no choice in 2001, up from 68 percent in 2000. In the remaining rural areas, 94 percent had no choice, up from 91 percent in 2000. Many plans, of course, simply can't find enough providers in these counties to form a viable network. However, despite the greater increases in capitation rates in rural areas, a number of plan withdrawals can *still* be traced to insufficient Medicare reimbursement.

The Other Medicare+Choice Options

Not surprisingly, as of 2002, very few new types of organizations had entered an M+C program plagued by capitation and policy problems. Under the category of managed care, two PPOs (Preferred Provider Organizations) and two PSOs (Provider Sponsored Organizations) have joined; under the category of nonmanaged care, one private fee-for-service plan—offered by Sterling Life Insurance Company—and *no* medical savings accounts have entered the program.

Though touted as a "revolutionary innovation" in Medicare, **Private Fee-for-Service (PFFS)** plans were widely available as the standard form of health insurance before the inception of Medicare. At that time PFFS plans yielded highly favorable results: coverage that could be tailored to the consumer's circumstances, wide patient choice, and market-directed pricing of health care goods and services. Since PFFS worked then, we might expect it to work again if allowed to develop as the market dictates.

In the PFFS arrangement, Medicare pays a set amount of money every month to a private company to provide coverage to people with Medicare on a pay-per-visit arrangement. PFFS works somewhat like the original Medicare plan with a supplemental medigap policy—that is, patients may go to any hospital or doctor of their choosing on a fee-for-service basis, can go outside their service area, and at minimum receive the services covered by Medicare Part A and Part B. Here the similarity ends. Under PFFS, the private insurer—not Medicare—decides how much to reimburse for the services you receive. You pay the monthly Part B premium, any additional monthly premium the PFFS plan charges above the Part B premium, any additional premium for extra benefits, and any plan deductible and copayment amounts, which can differ from those under the original Medicare plan.

As legislated, a **Medicare Medical Savings Account (MSA)** plan includes both a tax-free savings account and a health policy that has a high deductible (no more than $6,000). Medicare pays a fixed amount into the plan, footing the entire health-policy premium and depositing the remaining money into the savings account, which you use to pay your "qualifying" medical bills. Once you have met the deductible, the health policy pays.

In all likelihood, the amount of money in your savings account would be less than the plan's deductible for the first few years. If you use all the money in your Medicare MSA before you reach the plan's deductible, you must make up the difference out-of-pocket. Thus, even though MSAs cover the critical back-end expenses and would permit elderly health care consumers to manage their own health-related finances to a much larger extent than other alternatives, these plans may never catch on because they do not provide the popular front-end coverage that Americans have come to expect from their medical insurance.

Private Contracts

Perhaps the most controversial provision under Medicare Part C is the "private contracts option," which permits Medicare enrollees to contract privately, independent of Medicare, with physicians of their choosing. Medicare would pay none of the physician's charges and it would be the responsibility of the patient to negotiate fees under such contracts, unfettered by any price regulations.

Prior to M+C, Medicare patients had long obtained medical services outside the Medicare program—for both Medicare-covered services and services not covered by Medicare. However, confusion arose as to whether "excess fee restrictions" imposed by Federal and state law applied to Medicare-covered services delivered outside the Medicare program. The original intent of adding the private-contracting option to the Medicare Part C legislation, according to the bill's sponsors, was to make it explicit that Medicare patients had the right to contract privately with a doctor of their choice for medical services for which no claim for payment is submitted to Medicare—regardless of whether the care was a Medicare-covered service or not. The logic was that patients had a right to contract privately for medical care services, and any restrictions regarding excess fees did not apply if Medicare wasn't billed.

The final Medicare Part C legislation did include a provision for private contracting between doctors and patients. However, a hitch—known as Section 4507—was attached to the bill with virtually no publicity or debate. Section 4507 prohibits Medicare patients from going outside Medicare for Medicare-covered services and paying for them out of pocket *unless the doctor who provides the services forswears any Medicare program involvement for at least 2 years.* Of course, Medicare patients are free to obtain *noncovered* services on their own if they choose to pay for the service themselves.

Section 4507 is supposed to prevent doctors from treating both Medicare patients and Medicare-eligible private patients at the same time. The fear, held by those opposed to patients being able to contract privately for Medicare-covered services, is that it would lead to a two-tier system with private patients getting more and better medical care for Medicare covered services than their Medicare-pay counterparts. It was also asserted that under such private arrangements there would be "no limit" to what a physician might charge a patient.

From an economic perspective, this argument reveals a profound ignorance of market processes. Rather than a two-tier system, what is more likely to develop is a no-tier system. For instance, a specialist who has opted out of Medicare because he or she contracts privately with Medicare-eligible patients may be willing but unable under Section 4507 to take on a Medicare-pay patient. In addition, as we have observed in relation to many other transactions: "for every seller there must be a buyer." The market for medical services is no exception, and in voluntary transactions, the price of *anything* has a limit, namely, what the buyer will pay. If market transactions actually revealed that the prices physicians were able to get for their services were "exorbitantly high," the forces of supply and demand soon would provide more doctors seeking those prices, and fees would collapse. If allowed to develop unfettered, a genuinely private medical services market almost surely would, all else equal, see a slower rate of increase in medical costs.

What Should You Do?

Currently, America's senior citizens have very limited experience with M+C options other than HMOs. Very often it is the newest products to reach the healthcare market that carry the highest costs to consumers (as with, say, long-term care policies when they first

57

were introduced, partly because providers lack claims and loss experience). On the other hand, sometimes "getting in on the ground floor" is the best way to save money. For the healthcare consumer, this situation may further complicate the task of finding the lowest-cost protection against the expense of illness and incapacity.

In these circumstances, seniors should remain as flexible as possible. Even currently available coverage and premiums could change markedly if a significant portion of current Medicare subscribers choose one type of plan over another. But whatever options eventually reach the market, the underlying financial considerations discussed in the previous chapters will not change: *cover the major risks first*, which means acquiring the most comprehensive tail-end coverage available, whomever the provider may be.

VI.

MEDICARE SUPPLEMENTAL INSURANCE

S INCE July 31, 1992, any insurer offering Medicare Supplemental Insurance has been required to restrict policy offerings
to ten "approved" policies labeled A through J as stipulated by
federal and subsequent state regulations. In 1997, Congress allowed
insurers to offer a high-deductible option ($1,620 in 2003) for plans
F and J. This does not mean that insurance companies are prohibited
from selling other types of policies. But they may not be called
"Medicare Supplemental Insurance."

In this chapter we describe the major provisions of each of these
ten policies. With the important exceptions noted below, in states
that have approved the National Association of Insurance Commissioners (NAIC) model regulation, any Medicare Supplemental Insurance policy offered for sale must adhere strictly to those provisions. (Different types of policies are sold in Massachusetts, Minnesota, and Wisconsin because these states already required standardized medigap policies prior to 1992. If you reside in one of these
states, contact your State Insurance Department for more information—see Chapter VII.) The intent of the framers of these new model
standards was to simplify the medigap insurance decisions of consumers by requiring that insurers offer policies that are strictly comparable, thus permitting accurate "price shopping."

However, certain loopholes may permit insurers to tinker with
the NAIC standardized policies. According to the NAIC regulation, "The issuer of a Medicare supplement policy may, with the
prior approval of the [State] commissioner [of insurance], offer
new or innovative benefits in addition to the benefits provided in a
policy that otherwise complies with the applicable standards." And
according to the Omnibus Budget Reconciliation Act of 1990, is-
suers of Medicare supplement policies are not prohibited from
offering discounts to policyholders "for the purchase of items or
services not covered under its Medicare supplement policies (for
example: discounts on hearing aids or eyeglasses)." In short, the
insurers may simply find new ways to make their medigap policies
unique—which would largely defeat the intent of the "simplified"
NAIC regulations.

Table 2
NAIC MEDICARE SUPPLEMENT PLAN STANDARDS

Benefit	A	B	C	D	E	F[2]	G	H	I	J[2]
Core[1]	✓	✓	✓	✓	✓	✓	✓	✓	✓	✓
Part A (hospital) deductible		✓	✓	✓	✓	✓	✓	✓	✓	✓
Skilled nursing facility			✓	✓	✓	✓	✓	✓	✓	✓
Foreign emergency care			✓	✓	✓	✓	✓	✓	✓	✓
Part B (physician) deductible			✓			✓				✓
Part B (physician) excess charges						100%	80%		100%	100%
At-home recovery care				✓			✓		✓	✓
Prescription drugs								Basic[3]	Basic[3]	Ext'd[3]
Preventive screening					✓					✓
Average Annual Premium[4]	$949	1,206	1,470	1,263	1,221	1,504	1,313	2,828	2,710	2,584
Distribution of Sales[5]	13.2%	6.8	19.3	6.8	3.2	36.8	5.1	1.0	2.4	3.7

[1] Core benefits include: Part A (hospital) coinsurance plus a lifetime maximum benefit for an additional 365 days; Part B (physician) coinsurance, subject to the Part B deductible; and the first three (3) pints of blood each year. [2] Plans F and J also have a high deductible option ($1,620 in 2003). [3] Basic coverage: After you pay $250 per year deductible, the plan pays 50% of prescription drug costs up to a maximum of $1,250 per year ($3,000 per year for extended coverage). [4] Weiss Ratings, 2002. [5] NAIC, 2002, figures for 2001.

The Ten NAIC Approved
Medicare Supplemental Insurance Plans

However, the NAIC regulation is very specific about the benefits that the ten approved policies *must* contain. Any insurer who wants to sell Medicare Supplemental Insurance in a state must offer a basic policy (Policy A) that contains only the "core" benefits that are common to all approved policies. Insurers who offer the core policy may or may not offer any or all of the other approved policies that contain additional benefits. However, no policy may duplicate coverage that is provided by either Medicare Part A or Part B. (You do not need to buy a medigap policy if you are in a Medicare managed-care plan or if you are covered by Medicaid. Generally, in such cases, it is not legal for anyone to sell you one.) The terms of coverage provided by the ten Medicare Supplemental Insurance policies approved in the NAIC model regulation are summarized in Table 2 on page 60. The specific provisions of each of the policies are as follows. (A review of Medicare Part A and B coverage, explained in Chapter II, may be helpful at this point.)

Plan A (core policy) provides: The Medicare co-payment (in year 2003) of $210 per day for hospital stays for days 61–90 and $420 per day for days 91–150; up to 365 days of hospital expenses during your lifetime once Medicare Part A hospital benefits are used up; the Medicare co-payment (generally 20 percent of doctors' services) under Medicare Part B after you have met the $100 deductible; and the first 3 pints of blood each year

Plan A thus provides basic coverage for the hospitalization costs of catastrophic illness up to a year after Medicare benefits cease and for medical costs for all Medicare-approved charges. All 10 Medicare Supplemental Insurance policies must contain these core benefits.

In addition, as outlined in the table on page 60, **Plans B-J** must cover the Part A hospital deductible—$840 in 2003. Following that, **Plans C-J**, must cover the co-payment for skilled nursing-home care for days 21-100 ($105 a day in 2003) and medically necessary emergency care in a foreign country (80 percent of the cost during the first 60 days of each trip after $250 deductible, $50,000 lifetime limit). Plans C-J also provide an assortment of additional benefits, depending on the plan, as described below.

Plan C includes the Part B Medical Insurance deductible ($100 per year).

Plan D includes at-home recovery ($40 per visit to a maximum of $1,600 per year; doctor certification required).

Plan E includes preventive screening and care.

Plan F includes 100 percent of excess charges under Part B Medical Insurance (*i.e.*, the difference between your doctor's charge and Medicare's approved charge if your doctor does not accept assignment).

Plan F also has a high-deductible option ($1,620 in 2002) that covers 100 percent of covered out-of-pocket expenses (other than premiums). The prescription drug deductible must be met as well. After 2002, the deductible increases by the percentage increase in the Consumer Price Index for all urban consumers (CPI-U) for the 12-month period ending with August of the preceding year.

Plan G includes at-home recovery care and 80 percent of excess charges under Part B Medical Insurance.

Plan H includes coverage of 50 percent of the cost of outpatient prescription drugs after a $250 deductible, up to a maximum benefit of $1,250.

Plan I includes at-home recovery care, 100 percent of excess charges under Part B Medical Insurance, and 50 percent of the cost of outpatient prescription drugs after a $250 deductible, up to a maximum benefit of $1,250.

Plan J includes at-home recovery care, 100 percent of excess charges under Part B Medical Insurance, preventive screening and care, and 50 percent of the cost of outpatient prescription drugs after a $250 deductible, up to a maximum benefit of $3,000.

Plan J also has a high-deductible option ($1,620 in 2002) that covers 100 percent of covered out-of-pocket expenses (other than premiums). The prescription drug deductible must be met as well. After 2002, the deductible increases by the percentage increase in the Consumer Price Index for all urban consumers (CPI-U) for the 12-month period ending with August of the preceding year.

What is Medicare SELECT?

Medicare SELECT was introduced on a trial basis in 15 states in

1994, expanded to all 50 states in 1995, and made permanent in 1998. If you buy a Medicare SELECT policy, you are buying one of the 10 standardized medigap plans A through J. With a Medicare SELECT policy, you must use specific hospitals and in some cases specific doctors to get full insurance benefits (except in an emergency). For this reason, Medicare SELECT premiums are typically lower than comparable medigap policies that do not have this selected-provider feature; in 1999, SELECT premiums averaged $979, more than $200 less than the average premium for a standardized plan. About 9 percent of medigap enrollees had a SELECT plan in 1999, and NAIC reports that 15 states did not have an insurer selling such plans. For more information call your state insurance department (see Chapter VII).

How Much Does Medigap Insurance Cost?

Costs vary from plan to plan, from insurance company to insurance company, and from state to state. Hence, it is in your financial interest to shop around. The table on page 60 shows the average annual premium for each of the various standardized plans as of 2002. According to Weiss Ratings, Floridians pay the highest average premiums for Plans A through G, while Arkansas has the highest average premiums for Plans H, I, and J. Weiss also found a broad range in premiums for the same plan depending on the insurer. For example, for a 65-year-old woman: Plan A costs between $766 and $2,028 in Florida; Plan F varies between $877 and $2,487 in Texas; and Plan J ranges from $2,878 to $9,376 in Arkansas. Weiss also reported that the rise in average premium rates for medigap slowed to 2.4 percent in 2002, compared with annual average increases of 10.9 percent in 2001 and 7.2 percent in 2000.

When comparing premiums, you should try to estimate your likely costs over a 5- or 10-year period; what you pay when you first buy a policy and what it costs in the future depending on the method used to price the policy. If a policy is "community rated," all policy holders, regardless of age, pay the same premium. Companies are required to sell community-rated policies in Connecticut, Maine, Massachusetts, Minnesota, New York, and Washington. If a policy is "issue-age rated," the premium will depend on the age of the beneficiary at the time the policy is purchased. Florida and Georgia require companies to sell this type of policy.

Most medigap policies today, however, are "attained-age rated." With attained-age policies, premiums rise as you get older. For example, while the initial premium for an attained-age policy is generally lower than that of either a community-rated or issue-age rated policy, just the opposite situation usually develops as the beneficiary ages; an attained-age policy with an attractive premium at age 65 may not turn out to be the same bargain when you reach age 70 or 75.

Depending on the insurance company, your gender, smoking habits, and marital status may also affect your premiums. And, of course, none of the aforementioned pricing methods take into account the unpredictable but always upward pressure of both inflation and capricious government regulation.

The Relative Value of Plan Options

What you pay for a medigap policy largely depends on how much coverage you want—the more the coverage, the more the cost. You should not, however, purchase the most comprehensive policy just because you can afford the premiums—one plan may not be worth the additional premiums you would pay for it.

There are five benefits you need to consider when comparing Plans C-J, as shown in the table on page 60: Part B deductible; Part B excess charge; at-home recovery care; prescription drugs; and preventive screening. However, the Part B deductible ($100) and preventive screening benefits ($120) are minor expenses and so are less important than the other remaining options—Part B excess charges, at-home recovery, and prescription drugs.

At-home recovery benefits are also quite limited, paying no more than $40 per visit and $1,600 per year. In order to receive this benefit, you must be receiving Medicare-covered home health services already. Medicare coverage may be ample for the same services that the at-home recovery benefit would cover. Unless you are considering the costly prescription-drug benefit (see below), in which case at-home recovery would likely be a minor consideration, Plans D and G are your only choices for at-home recovery coverage.

If the Part B excess-charge benefit (potentially much greater than the at-home recovery benefit) is important to you, then you cannot choose a plan that will pay 100 percent of those charges if you also want at-home recovery coverage; instead, you will be limited to Plan G, which provides only 80 percent coverage of Part B excess charges. Though Part B excess charges are now somewhat less important than they were because of federal and state limitations on balance billing, they can still be formidable. For instance, $115,000 worth of physician bills that were 15 percent above Medicare's allowed charge would leave you with a liability of $15,000. And, unlike the at-home recovery coverage, Part B excess-charge benefits are not capped.

Your decision on coverage may, therefore, be simplified, particularly if you have some idea of your particular risks relating to Part B excess charges and prescription drugs, since these are the two benefits that could make the largest difference in your costs, assuming you are choosing a policy from Plan C through Plan J. If you think Part B excess charges are likely to be important, Plans F, I, or J give maximum benefits; Plan G provides the 80 percent benefit.

If you think prescription drugs are likely to be important, Plans H and I give basic coverage; Plan J gives extended coverage. However, the prescription drug benefit makes these plans expensive. According to Weiss Ratings, the premiums for all three medigap plans with prescription-drug coverage (Plans H, I, and J) averaged more than $2,500. Because of the deductible ($250) and 50 percent coinsurance, you would have to spend at least $2,750 a year for drugs to get the full $1,250 benefit for Plans H and I. For Plan J, you must spend $6,250 a year on prescription drugs to get the full $3,000 benefit.

Is drug coverage worth it to you? To answer the question, you must first estimate your annual prescription costs. Plans H, I, and J all impose a $250 deductible for drugs, with Plans H and I covering half the drug costs up to $2,500 per year, and Plan J covering half of such costs up to $6,000 annually. In other words, Plans H and I pay a maximum $1,250 drug benefit after the deductible is met, and Plan J pays $3,000. Thus, you would have to spend more than $2,750 a year to get the maximum benefit from Plans H and I, and at least $6,250 per year on prescription drugs.

Plans F and C are the most widely held plans (combined 58 percent) and identical except that Plan F covers Part B excess charges. Neither plan covers at-home recovery or prescription drugs. Plan F costs on average $34 more than Plan C.

Beware the "Hard Sell"

Whenever major changes occur in a program such as Medicare, opportunities are created for the insurance companies to exploit a newly created market. Today, the "Medicare roller coaster" has created just such an opportunity and, not surprisingly, the sales forces of most health insurers have marshaled their considerable talents to convince Medicare subscribers that they need their company's policy. As in all such situations, exaggeration of risks and benefits sometimes plays a part in the sales presentation. We review below a number of tactics—and potential sales abuses—to which consumers should be alert.

"Lead cards." Reportedly, Medicare subscribers in many states are being mailed what are called "lead cards" in order to identify potential supplemental insurance buyers. Usually, these mailings come in official-looking envelopes with an official-sounding name that conveys the impression the sender is connected with a Government agency. The enclosed letter may warn of supposed great risks faced by the elderly as a result of changes in Medicare and usually offers the addressee important information if the enclosed form is filled out (stating name, address, age, Social Security number, and the like) and returned to the sender. Often, the subject of insurance is not mentioned in the lead card, but that is the purpose of the mailing.

In fact, the names and addresses that are returned on the cards to the marketing firm are then sold to insurance companies or their agents as "hot prospects" for Medicare supplemental insurance or "alternative" insurance policies. Some states, such as California, have clamped down on these practices. If you receive such a mailing, you should be aware that if you return the card, in all likelihood your name will be sold to an insurer who then will try to sell you a policy.

Appeals to urgency. Insurance salespersons may stress that you must "act now" to get the most coverage from a particular insurance policy. However, once a policy prospectus has been developed, the terms of coverage for that policy will not change no matter how long a buyer waits to purchase it. High-pressure sales techniques that stress the urgency of acquiring a particular policy simply are designed to get you to purchase as soon as possible.

In some situations, however, it may make sense to buy a policy sooner rather than later. For example, if you have decided that a policy provides adequate coverage at a reasonable cost, and if premium costs will increase if, say, you become a year older (for insurance purposes) at an imminent birth date, it will save you money to sign the insurance contract before that time.

Duplicate coverage. The NAIC Model Standards prevent supplemental policies from duplicating Medicare benefits, but they do not address the sale of policies that may replicate *other* supplemental policies. Although it violates most states' fair sales practices legislation, insurance sales personnel may try to find a way around the rules and sell you what amounts to duplicate coverage. For example, the salesperson may not inquire if you already own a Medicare supplemental policy, and if challenged later be able to say that he or she was unaware that the policy offered replicated existing coverage. Or the sales pitch may emphasize that the offered policy provides additional coverage from the supplemental policy you own and that both are needed to provide "comprehensive protection." Do not be deceived by such appeals. You should look for the best supplemental policy for your circumstances and buy that policy and only that policy.

"Mining for gold." Beware of salespeople who immediately try to find out how much you are worth. They may want to know how large a policy they can sell, not what may be the best buy for you. Do not offer information about your personal finances. After all alternatives have been explored and you have had a chance to compare a number of different policies at your leisure and out of the watchful eye of the salesperson, you may want to review how much insurance you can afford with a *disinterested* third party (your financial adviser or banker, for example). But opening your financial account books to the insurance salesperson may invite sales abuses.

Evaluating the Insurers

Industry specialists generally agree about what the future of health care insurance holds: higher premiums, rate increases, restructured benefit offerings, additional "out-of-pocket" expenses, continued growth in the size of the uninsured population, more mergers and acquisitions, amended prescription benefits, and more failures by healthcare companies. Furthermore, a host of regulatory and performance issues will affect various products and markets.

The combination of sharply rising health-care costs, Government regulation, actuarial imprecision, and managerial confusion has resulted in substantial underwriting losses for some insurers in the past decade or so. (Underwriting losses occur when companies pay out more in benefits and operating expenses than they take in as premium income.) One might well question how insurance companies can continue in business after taking losses. All insurance companies have two sources of income—premiums and investments. For most of the last decade, premium income was inadequate to cover benefit expenditures. Until recently, investment income more than made up for premium losses. However, investment gains no longer offset underwriting losses.

Heavy reliance on unstable investment returns made insurers especially vulnerable when health care costs and benefit payments continued to increase while offsetting yields on investments became harder to achieve. In short, many insurance companies now find themselves in a classic financial squeeze, a situation that has led some industry analysts to speculate that "shakeouts" may occur—that is, weaker companies will be forced out of business or merged with healthier ones.

You do have some protection in case the industry squeeze affects your policy. If your medigap coverage ceases because of the bankruptcy or insolvency of your insurer, federal law gives you the right to buy either Medigap Plan A, B, C, or F within 63 days of the date you lose your coverage, provided the Medigap plan is offered in your state. The insurance company cannot deny you the policy, place conditions on the policy such as a waiting period, apply a preexisting condition exclusion, or discriminate in the price of the policy based on your health status. Make sure you keep a copy of your plan's termination letter. (Some states provide more medigap protection than federal law.) These guarantees may be of small comfort to you if your previous medigap policy was in a plan other than Plan A, B, C, or F and you still desire the benefits of that plan. Furthermore, if your new policy is not community rated, you may face a premium penalty.

Therefore, carefully ascertain that the policy you are considering is offered by a healthy insurer—and that it is likely to return good value. With respect to insurer health, we recommend that policies be purchased only from companies that are rated "A+" or "A++" by

Best's Insurance Reports. Best's Reports represent an opinion based on a comprehensive quantitative and qualitative evaluation of a company's financial strength, operating performance, and market profile. (Chapter VII discusses how to use *Best's Reports.*)

Another useful measure of both the financial health of a company and the value that it returns to policyholders is the so-called loss ratio, which represents the percentage of premiums that are returned to policyholders as benefits. Many state departments of insurance (see listing in Chapter VII) have prepared brief guides to supplemental health insurance for Medicare subscribers. And a number of these advise supplemental insurance buyers to use insurance companies' loss ratios as a way to compare the relative value of policies. Low loss ratios indicate that a policy is not returning value to policyholders. Federal law stipulates that a cumulative 65 percent loss ratio for individual policies (75 percent for group policies) must be met over the life of a policy, which is assumed to be 15 years. Insurers are required to pay refunds or provide credits to policyholders when policies fail to meet loss ratio standards.

Table 3 on page 70 shows the underwriting loss ratios of the 50 largest writers (by premiums) of accident and health insurance in 1999 (latest data available). As that table illustrates, the majority of companies writing policies in the accident and health insurance field currently are posting underwriting loss ratios that are high. Traditionally, insurance actuaries aim for underwriting loss ratios in the range of 70 to 75 percent. Losses in this range allow a company to retain an attractive marketing stance, yet still permit the company to turn an acceptable underwriting profit. Losses much over 75 percent, however, may be risky to the company—and here a difference of a few percentage points can make the difference between profit and loss, and, eventually, between solvency and insolvency. In 1999, 30 of the 50 largest insurers posted loss ratios above 80 percent, by conventional standards a somewhat risky level. Also in 1999, according to the Government Accounting Office, the 15 largest sellers of medigap policies had loss ratios ranging from 64 to 88 percent.

In short, be sure to check out the financial health as well as the benefits and premium costs of any insurer whose policy you are considering. Even the best coverage at a low price will be useless if the company cannot pay claims promptly (or at all).

Table 3
UNDERWRITING LOSS AND EXPENSE RATIOS OF THE
50 LARGEST WRITERS OF ACCIDENT AND HEALTH INSURANCE

Rank	Company/Group	Loss Ratio	Expense Ratio
1	Aflac Inc/Group	83.0	29.7
2	UnitedHealth group	84.3	11.3
3	UnumProvident Group	96.0	39.2
4	Aetna Inc Group	72.2	19.8
5	Cigna Group	89.6	13.5
6	Health Care Service Corp	83.6	14.2
7	Conseco Insurance Group	80.2	30.1
8	Humana Inc	87.1	21.2
9	Guardian Group	83.1	23.3
10	Metropolitan Life & Affiliated	102.3	18.4
11	CNAInsurance Group	91.8	9.4
12	Fortis Inc Group	71.6	41.5
13	Principal Life Insurance Co	90.6	22.9
14	Blue Cross & Blue Shield FL Group	85.3	16.5
15	Trigon Healthcare Group	85.7	14.2
16	Mutual of Omaha Group	81.4	23.3
17	Anthem Group	84.4	12.5
18	American International Group	54.4	36.8
19	GE Financial Assurance Group	74.3	40.4
20	Wellmark Group	88.5	14.6
21	WellPoint Health Networks Inc	83.7	17.0
22	Hartford Life Inc	84.2	27.0
23	Aegon USA Inc	64.2	40.6
24	Great-West Life Group	60.1	38.6
25	Prudential of America Group	114.0	83.4
26	American Medical Security Group	81.1	22.9
27	Trustmark Group	83.2	26.8
28	Aon Corp	41.4	55.5
29	Torchmark Corp	69.9	29.3
30	Louisiana Health Services Group	91.2	12.7
31	American General Group	71.4	36.3
32	Blue Cross & Blue Shield KS Group	88.7	11.1
33	Arkansas BC & BS Group	83.6	17.7
34	JC Penney Group	38.1	56.1
35	Standard Insurance Co	80.8	27.2
36	UICI Group	67.2	34.2
37	Sun Life of Canada Group	118.0	35.7
38	Northwestern Mutual Group	77.2	33.8
39	Berkshire Hathaway Group	86.0	32.4
40	Blue Cross & Blue Shield of MO Group	79.8	20.9
41	Allianz Insurance Group	77.9	30.0
42	Physicians Mutual Group	66.4	32.2
43	Blue Cross & Blue Shield of MS Group	85.1	14.4
44	Golden Rule Group	75.8	23.2
45	Cuna Mutual Group	65.7	43.2
46	Oxford Health Ins Inc	80.5	22.9
47	Citigroup	78.1	26.7
48	Pacific Life Group	74.7	24.9
49	American National Group	73.5	40.5
50	New York Life Group	101.1	22.3

Source: Best's Review, December 2000.

VII.

SHOPPING FOR
A MEDICARE SUPPLEMENTAL POLICY

INSURANCE agents are trained to emphasize the advantages of their company's policies and the drawbacks of their competitors' products. Insurance salespeople hope to convince you that their policy represents the best value by "comparing" it with other policies. Do not be deceived. These sales-oriented comparisons often are designed to make one policy look much better than all the rest and are unreliable. In all likelihood, few, if any, companies will offer all ten medigap plans—and they will, no doubt, develop sales presentations that emphasize the benefits only of the plans they do offer.

Ultimately, it is up to you to find the best value through independent inquiry. Do not rely on salespeople and do not rely on friends who claim to have found a "great deal." Friends may be well-meaning, but they also may not have all the facts relevant to your situation.

Every State Is Different

Premium costs from company to company and from state to state vary widely. Even within some states, prices on the same policy are different. In fact, in the larger metropolitan areas of the Northeast and the Midwest, your premium cost may depend on the side of town in which you reside. In short, a policy that may represent the best value in one state or locality will not necessarily be the best value in another state or locality. You cannot rely on the advice of friends who reside outside your area.

A number of state insurance departments or related state agencies have consumer affairs divisions that provide information free to prospective medigap insurance buyers. As a first step in shopping for a Medicare supplemental policy, contact your state agency as shown in the directory in this chapter. Request a list of all Medicare supplemental insurance providers currently offering policies in your locality. Make certain you get current addresses and telephone numbers. Also, ask for any related literature. A number of states have prepared guides to supplemental insurance, and most contain pertinent information regarding the peculiarities of such insurance in their states.

You may also obtain a list of medigap providers in your area by calling 1-800-MEDICARE (1-800-633-4227) or by visiting the Medicare website at www.medicare.gov under the "Medigap Compare" tool, which also links you to the appropriate insurance company websites.

When you have obtained a list of Medicare supplemental insurance providers for your area, contact each one. Request full policy details, including coverage, exclusions or restrictions, waiting periods, renewability, and premium rates. If any policy does not meet the NAIC Model Standards or the additional requirements of your state, contact the State Insurance Department and report the discrepancy.

Using Best's Insurance Reports

To determine the status of each company for which you have a policy prospectus, consult *Best's Insurance Reports: Life and Health*. Even fewer insurance buyers know about *Best's* than about their state insurance department, but it is an equally useful resource. A. M. Best Co. is an independent insurance evaluator that publishes monthly and annual reports on a variety of issues regarding the insurance industry. The reference librarian in your local library will direct you to *Best's Reports*.

You want to consult *Best's Insurance Reports: Life and Health* for the most recent year available. This will be a large, heavy, red bound volume that resembles an encyclopedia in looks and contains nearly as much information. (Many libraries also carry it in electronic form.) *Best's Reports* lists virtually all insurance companies currently writing policies in the United States. *Best's* rates each company on a letter grade: "A++" and "A+" (superior), "A" and "A–" (excellent), "B++" and "B+" (very good), "B" and "B–" (good), "C++" and "C+" (fair), "C" and "C–" (marginal), "D" (below minimum standards), "E" (under state supervision), and "F" (in liquidation). Any company with a B rating or lower is being "damned with faint praise." As a general rule, it is advisable to insure only with those companies rated superior (A+ or A++).

Ratings are also available from Standard and Poor's Ratings Group,

Fitch Ratings, and Weiss Ratings, Inc. Ratings are available by phone or online: A. M. Best Company, (908) 439-2200, www.ambest.com; Fitch Ratings, (212) 908-0500. www.fitchratings.com; Standard & Poor's, (212) 438-2400, www.standardandpoors.com; Weiss Research, Inc., (800) 289-9222, www.weissratings.com. Quotesmith (www.quotesmith.com) provides free instant Medicare supplement insurance quotes from up to 28 companies along with the latest A. M. Best, Fitch Ratings, Moody's, Standard & Poor's, and Weiss ratings for each company.

What You Should Ask the Insurance People Before You Buy

A policy may look good on paper, but if the company refuses for one reason or another to pay the promised benefit, or if benefits come so slowly that they cause you worry, inconvenience, and embarrassment, you may want to avoid that policy—no matter how low the premiums or how high the supposed coverage. Therefore, you should investigate the claims response record of the company before you purchase a policy. The important facts are generally not published, and you may need to ask the insurance agent the following questions:

- **What is the loss ratio on the policy (or on a similar policy if the policy you are considering is new) for the past few years?** This figure may differ from the "anticipated loss ratio" usually cited in promotional literature. If the actual figure is much lower than the anticipated figure, ask why.

- **How long, on average, does it take to process a claim and for you or your doctor or hospital to receive payment?** It can be worrisome and costly if benefits arrive inordinately slowly. Ask where your claim will go and who has to approve it. Are authorizations made locally, or are all claims forwarded to the "head office"?

- **What percentage of claims is reduced and what percentage is denied on the policy you are investigating? Why have such claims been reduced or denied?** The overwhelming majority of insurers have scrupulous claims procedures, but a few have been known to try to cut losses through legal challenges to claims. You want to be certain that any policy you purchase will

73

NATIONAL DIRECTORY
OF STATE INSURANCE DEPARTMENTS

Write or telephone the State Insurance Department at the following locations:

Alabama, Montgomery 36130	334-269-3550
Alaska, Juneau 99811-3422	907-465-2515
Arizona, Phoenix 85018	602-912-8444
Arkansas, Little Rock 72201	501-371-2600
California, Sacramento 95814	916-322-3887
Colorado, Denver 80202	303-894-7499
Connecticut, Hartford 06142-0816	860-297-3800
Delaware, Dover 19904	302-739-4251
D.C., Washington 20004	202-727-1000
Florida, Tallahassee 32399-0300	850-413-3100
Georgia, Atlanta 30334	404-656-2056
Hawaii, Honolulu 96813	808-586-2790
Idaho, Boise 83720-0043	208-334-4250
Illinois, Springfield 62767	217-782-4515
Indiana, Indianapolis 46204-2787	317-232-2385
Iowa, Des Moines 50319	515-281-5705
Kansas, Topeka 66612-1678	785-296-3071
Kentucky, Frankfort 40602	502-564-3630
Louisiana, Baton Rouge 70804-9214	225-342-5825
Maine, Augusta 04333	207-624-8500
Maryland, Baltimore 21202-2272	410-468-2000
Massachusetts, Boston 02216	617-973-8787
Michigan, Lansing 48917-4850	517-335-4978
Minnesota, St. Paul 55101	651-296-4026
Mississippi, Jackson 39201	601-359-3569
Missouri, Jefferson City 65102-1527	573-751-4815
Montana, Helena 59601	406-444-2040
Nebraska, Lincoln 68505-3639	402-471-2201
Nevada, Carson City 89701	775-687-4270
New Hampshire, Concord 03301-7317	603-271-2261
New Jersey, Trenton 08625-0325	609-292-5360
New Mexico, Albequerque 87110	505-255-0971
New York, Albany 12257	518-474-6600
North Carolina, Raleigh 27611	919-733-7343
North Dakota, Bismarck 58505-0320	701-328-2440

Ohio, Columbus 43215 614-644-2658
Oklahoma, Oklahoma City 73152-3408 405-521-2828
Oregon, Salem 97301-3883 503-947-4351
Pennsylvania, Harrisburg 17120 877-881-6388
Rhode Island, Providence 02903 401-222-2223

South Carolina, Columbia 29223 803-737-6160
South Dakota, Pierre 57501 605-773-3563
Tennessee, Nashville 37243 615-741-2241
Texas, Austin 78701-9104 512-463-6169
Utah, Salt Lake City 84114-1010 801-538-6101

Vermont, Montpelier 05620-3101 802-828-3301
Virginia, Richmond 23219 804-371-9741
Washington, Olympia 98504-0255 360-753-7301
West Virginia, Charleston 25305-0540 304-558-3354
Wisconsin, Madison 53702 608-266-3585
Wyoming, Cheyenne 82002 307-777-7401

pay benefits promptly as promised.

- **What are your rights as a policyholder if your claim is reduced or denied?**

- **Is the claim form straightforward and simple, or overly complex?** Ask to see a copy if you will be required to file it yourself (see next paragraph).

- **Who will be paid benefits, you or the health care provider?** Generally, you save time and trouble if the company will pay the doctor directly. Many doctors have arrangements with insurers so that you need not bother filing claim forms. Others have no such arrangements, and you must take care of the bills and file for your insurance benefits. If you are still ill when the bills start to come in, this task can be burdensome.

- **If the company will pay benefits directly to the health care provider, how will you be notified that payments have been made?** This is important, since all too often the doctor's office will mistakenly continue to bill you for charges already paid by your insurance. You need evidence that the bill has been paid. Also, the absence of notification will alert you that the company may not have paid the bill.

75

- **How are claims for treatment out-of-state or outside your "prevailing charges area" evaluated?** Many insurance companies calculate premiums based on actuarial estimates for a limited geographical area. Some of them will pay only the "prevailing charges" of your area even though the charges in other areas may be higher, leaving you at substantial risk. For example, if you reside in a rural or suburban area and are stricken with an illness that requires emergency surgery in a large metropolitan area, the difference in coverage from one "prevailing charge" area to the other could easily amount to hundreds, if not thousands of dollars. The incidence of illness among seniors is statistically greater during holiday visits with relatives and friends than at other times. You certainly want to be protected during those times.

Your questioning may very well make the insurance representative uncomfortable, but it is your right and in your interest to ask. If the salesperson is uncooperative or if he is pleasant but never provides you the information you want, do not do business with that person.

Open Enrollment Requirement

The NAIC Medicare Model legislation requires that new Medicare subscribers be allowed a 6-month "open enrollment" period in which they cannot be denied Medicare Supplemental Insurance because of their health status, previous claims history, or medical condition. Section 11 of the NAIC Model Standards provisions states: "No issuer of Medicare supplement policies in this state may deny or condition the issuance or effectiveness of any Medicare supplement policy available for sale in this state, nor may it discriminate in the pricing of such policy because of the health status, claims experience, receipt of health care, or medical condition of an applicant where an application for such policy is submitted during the six (6) month period beginning with the first month in which an individual (who is 65 years of age or older) first enrolled for benefits under Medicare Part B." Most states now have adopted such legislation.

Take advantage of this window of opportunity. If you don't, you may not be able to get the policy you want, may face a preexisting-condition limitation, may have to pay more for any given policy, or may even run the risk of not being able to buy a policy at all. This point cannot be overemphasized—**once you sign up for Medicare Part B, make sure you don't miss the six-month open-enrollment period for purchasing a Medicare supplement insurance policy.**

What You Should Tell the Insurance People Before You Buy

Even with the open enrollment guarantee, the medical history that you will be required to submit when applying for a policy constitutes an integral part of the insurance contract. If that medical history can be demonstrated to have been willfully falsified, the insurance contract may not be legally binding.

It is therefore crucial that you complete the medical history form accurately. Do not be concerned about reporting illness that required hospitalization, surgery, or other treatment in the past. A person who reaches age 65 with no prior history of illness is the exception, not the rule.

Do not think that because you may not have to submit to a physical examination, your health history is not of consequence to the insurance company. It is. That is why the health history you complete becomes a part of the contract.

Even though you may sign a contract, pay premiums, and be issued a policy, an incorrect health history could mean that you have absolutely no insurance.

Unfortunately, all too many of the claims difficulties retired people have reported in the past were their own fault. Policyholders have paid hundreds and hundreds of dollars in premiums only to have their claims legally denied by the insurance company when illness struck. In most of these cases, the claimants either gave false information or withheld pertinent information of which they had knowledge when they completed their applications for insurance.

Therefore, answer all questions regarding your health honestly and completely. This does not mean that you will be required to recall everything that happened to you in the past. But as a matter of contractual integrity, you are obliged to do the best you can. To do otherwise places you at enormous risk.

77

VIII.

RANKING THE NAIC POLICIES BY COST AND RISK

DESPITE the "simplification" of medigap insurance through the NAIC's delineation of ten standard policies, it can still be difficult to determine which policy offers the best value for a particular individual. Of course, the task of comparing similar policies has been made immeasurably easier—other things being equal, for identical policies the one with the lowest premium is the best value. But that type of comparison does not determine which options might be most valuable to individual consumers. Indeed, advice about the value of different coverage options often is vague and subjective. Although we know of no foolproof way to evaluate the relative values of the health insurance policies now on the market, we try here to provide a procedure that can be applied to virtually anyone's circumstance.

Many state insurance departments or related state agencies (see Chapter VII) provide booklets to help you compare the NAIC supplemental policies. These usually include two or three pages of comparison worksheets for you to fill in policy options and compare prices. The guide, "Choosing a Medigap Policy"—available through the national Medicare hotline at 1-800-MEDICARE (1-800-633-4227) or on the Medicare website at www.medicare.gov—walks you through six "steps to buying a medigap policy" and includes three worksheets. These guides advise you to "weigh each option carefully" and to "decide which is best for you." Unfortunately, they usually do not tell you *how* to weigh options or *how* to arrive at an informed decision regarding them. With little or no help, you are asked to compare different options whose value to you remains unknown. Here we try to be more specific.

When evaluating health insurance, risk and cost should be your overriding concerns. Since the purpose of health insurance is to reduce financial risk, you must determine the extent to which any given policy would reduce this risk in the event of illness. Next, you must answer how much you will have to pay for this protection.

The cost-risk principle helps you to elect insurance that provides the most protection against risk at the lowest cost. The following is a simple expression of this principle, which we shall call the "cost-risk index," that allows you to compare the relative value of policies:

Cost-Risk Index = Cost x Risk

Cost is the annual premium on the policy. Many insurance companies quote monthly, quarterly, or semiannual premiums to make the amount seem more affordable. To convert these to an annual figure: multiply monthly amounts by 12, multiply quarterly premiums by 4, and multiply semiannual premiums by 2.

Risk is the amount you would owe for medical care after both Medicare and the supplemental policy had paid their benefits. To determine risk, design a hypothetical situation or situations in which you assume the need for a certain type of care and then calculate how much protection a policy would not provide in the event of such need. Although time-consuming, this is the most useful and least complicated way of calculating risk.

Obviously, the lower the *cost* and the lower the *risk,* the lower the *cost-risk index* and the better the value. A higher index indicates a poorer value.

Advantages of Multiple-Case Evaluation of Risk

Previous uses of hypothetical cases in the evaluation of Medicare supplemental insurance have relied mainly on a single-case risk design. That is, the determination of risk was based on only one hypothetical situation. Although a single-case design has some value and is not very time-consuming to develop, a multiple-case risk design can be more useful.

Multiple-case risk designs incorporate both the strengths and weaknesses in coverage over a number of policy provisions. (Single-case designs of necessity exclude one or more provisions from determination of risk.) Further, these designs allow flexibility and weighting. For instance, you can accommodate *average risks* based on the reported experience of the Medicare population, infrequent but potentially *catastrophic risks,* and the likelihood of *known risks* based on your own health history.

A wide variety of potentially ruinous illnesses require many different types of care—and hence insurance coverage. Thus the value of multiple-case designs, unlike single-case designs, can account for a number of potential risks.

The following risk design was determined after consultation with health care planners and with reference to the *Activity Reports* of the Commission on Professional and Hospital Activities. It incorporates both average risk experience and potential risk experience. Adhering to the health insurance principle, weight has been given to the potential risks. This design may be used as shown or adjusted to accommodate your own health situation:

Sample Risk Design

Case 1: Average Hospital Confinement
5-day hospitalization
Medical expense of $7,500

Case 2: Intermediate Hospital Confinement/
Intermediate Skilled Nursing Facility Confinement
21-day hospitalization
30-day skilled nursing facility confinement
Medical expense of $25,000

Case 3: Extended Hospital Confinement
100-day hospitalization
Medical expense of $85,000

Case 4: Extended Skilled Nursing Facility Confinement
16-day hospitalization
180-day skilled nursing facility confinement
Medical expense of $35,000

Case 5: Extended Hospital Confinement/
Extended Skilled Nursing Facility Confinement
180-day hospitalization
150-day skilled nursing facility confinement
Medical expense of $200,000

To determine the total risk associated with this risk design for each policy you are considering: (1) calculate probable daily hospital and skilled nursing facility costs for your locality by calling the billing department of your hospital or local nursing facility and requesting current daily charges; (2) calculate what you would still owe after the insurance benefits had been paid for each case; and then (3) sum these five amounts. That is your total estimated financial risk.

81

This "Sample Risk Design" accommodates a variety of hypothetical situations based on a distribution of both *potential* and *average* risks. However, it was figured *without* regard to individual health experience, which can have a significant bearing on the value of a particular policy. For persons whose health history indicates no particular risk, the sample risk design will indicate how different policies compare in relation to average risk experience; absent prior knowledge of illness or the likelihood of illness, averages permit a statistical assessment of intermediate risks. However, potential risks based on your own health history must always receive the greatest weight in the multiple-case evaluation of risk.

Your health history may suggest that your risks in some areas are greater than in others. If you know of an existing condition, or have parents and relatives who have been stricken with an illness requiring specific care, then you should use this knowledge to your advantage. If, for example, you or members of your family are prone to illness requiring long-term care in a skilled nursing facility, then your design ought to include such a hypothetical case. Or if you or members of your immediate family suffer from a chronic condition that requires regular physician visits and treatment, but not hospitalization or skilled nursing facility confinement, then your risk design ought to give more weight to that condition.

If you include potential risks in your risk design, then you can weight your evaluation toward your individual health risks. For the most part, however, this is a matter of "fine tuning" and is not likely to affect greatly the rank order of policies. In cases where there is a close decision to be made, however, it may suggest the more attractive alternative.

Using the Cost-Risk Index

In order to compare the relative values of specific policies, calculate the cost-risk index for each by multiplying the total risk as determined above by the annual premium amount.

The resulting cost-risk index rank (the indexes listed by magnitude) must be interpreted with discretion. It does not *prove* that one policy represents a "better value" than another. Rather, the index rank provides you only with one statistical indication of how different policies may or may not represent value in view of your own needs and resources.

Such indexes and rankings do, however, broadly indicate relative value. A policy with a relatively low cost-risk index *usually* means that it is a good value. Risk is by far the larger factor in the cost-risk formula, so that a low index nearly always indicates low risk. Low price and low risk determine good value. A policy with an intermediate index value might indicate any of several situations: (1) risk might be low, but price is high; (2) price might be low, but risk is relatively high; or (3) both price and risk are moderate.

A policy with a high index, however, *usually* indicates poor value. Either the risk is high, or the cost is high, or both. In general, the lower the cost-risk index, the better the value.

Part 3
LONG-TERM CARE OPTIONS

IX

LONG-TERM-CARE INSURANCE

ONE of the gnawing fears of older Americans is that they might end up in a nursing home—and go broke paying for it. These fears are fueled by insurance companies' promotional brochures that cite frightening statistics indicating that the chances of needing expensive long-term care are high. Among the claims are: "nearly 40 percent of people age 65 now are likely to spend some time in a nursing home," "the average cost of a year's stay in a nursing home is $56,000 and the actual cost can be much higher," "the average length of stay in a nursing home is nearly 3 years," and "half of all women and a third of all men who are now over 65 will spend their last years in a nursing home."

It may well be that the greatest nonmedical financial risk associated with aging is the cost of custodial nursing care. However, these statistics are misleading because the average stays are skewed by a small number of patients who stay for many years. Insurance companies overstate the risks of confinement and impoverishment in hopes of swaying the elderly to signing up for long-term-care insurance. Yet, despite the hype, less than 10 percent of individuals age 65 and older have purchased such insurance.

Many of the early nursing home policies were very high-priced indemnity contracts (contracts that pay a fixed-dollar amount per day) that provided limited coverage far below that required for protection against the catastrophic costs of long-term custodial care. In the past decade, however, some of the most objectionable features of earlier policies, such as those requiring prior hospitalization before admission to a nursing home or excluding coverage for nursing care required for Alzheimer's disease, have been eliminated, and many policies now cover not only care in a nursing home but also home health care. The wider range of benefits has made long-term-care insurance less restrictive than it once was. However, policies sold earlier may retain clauses that make them practically worthless as "insurance." You should review your policy's provisions and obtain modifications if necessary.

Unfortunately, long-term-care insurance is expensive. Because of the newness of this type of insurance, many policies have not yet had a significantly large number of claims filed, creating a challenging environment in which to set rates. According to Quotesmith.com, a 65-year-old male in 2003 can expect to pay in the range of $2,228–$4,260 per year for a policy with inflation protection that pays a $200 daily benefit for three years after a 90-day waiting period. Premiums rise steeply with age. A 75-year-old might pay $5,626–$9,880, assuming he qualified for the insurance. (The odds of being rejected or charged a higher premium due to health problems also climb steeply with age.)

Along with high premiums and uncertainty about the genuine risks of long-term care, confusion over complicated policies may help account for the relatively low sales. Long-term-care policies are not standardized like Medicare supplemental insurance, and insurers offer a complex assortment of benefits and coverage. In addition to nursing home coverage, policies may (or may not) cover respite care, hospice care, personal care in your home, services in assisted living facilities, services in adult day-care centers, or services in other community facilities. Home coverage may be limited to care from licensed home-health agencies, or it may pay for homemaker services and for unlicensed home-health-care aides to help with personal care.

More often than not, extras such as coverage for home care add substantially to your premium. Moreover, the benefit, which may be limited to care from licensed home health agencies, is normally half of the daily benefit for nursing home confinement, and when it comes to qualifying, the factors used to determine eligibility for nursing home care generally apply. Despite the allure of home-care coverage, you should carefully consider whether the amount you can afford with be adequate. A modest benefit that is payable only when you are substantially impaired is unlikely to keep you out of a nursing home.

The degree of impairment that triggers benefits varies widely as well. Insurers usually begin paying benefits when you become unable to perform one or more of the following "activities of daily living," called ADLs: bathing, dressing, eating, toileting, and transferring (getting out of a bed, a chair, etc.). In addition, most policies provide benefits for cognitive impairment. The standards for judging impairment, however, often vary among companies. Some pay benefits if you need "substantial assistance," e.g., someone has to dress you. Others require that you need "hands-on" assistance (someone to button your shirt) or "standby assistance" (someone within arm's reach while you dress yourself). Some insurers pay benefits if your doctor certifies that the care is medically necessary, regardless of cognitive limitations or ability to perform ADLs.

Once benefits are triggered, payments won't begin until after an elimination period (also called deductible or waiting period). This can be as long as 90 or 100 days after you start using long-term-care services or become disabled.

Some long-term-care policies are reimbursement contracts, meaning they pay for specific services received or expenses incurred up to a preset limit. Insurers also issue indemnity policies, which pay a set dollar amount regardless of the cost of the "covered care" you have been getting. A few companies may also issue disability policies, which only require that you meet your benefit trigger (level of disability) and pay even if you are not receiving any long-term-care services; you decide how to spend your money. For example, you can pay a relative or neighbor to provide care rather than having to go through a licensed home-health-care agency that is approved by the insurance company.

Unlike most health insurance contracts that have "open-ended benefits" generally not limited to any dollar amount, many long-term-care policies promise to pay only a fixed amount for a limited period and will not provide adequate protection against any genuinely catastrophic expense of long-term nursing-home care. Insurers normally pay benefits by the day, week, or month, and let you choose an amount that ranges from, say, $50 to $350 per day, $350 to $2,450 per week, or $1,500 to $10,500 per month. Most policies limit the total benefit they will pay over the life of the policy in terms of either the dollar amount or time (one, two, three years or more), but contracts with lifetime-benefits options have recently entered the market. These policies should begin to address the need for catastrophic coverage.

The Health Insurance Portability and Accountability Act of 1996 allows premiums for long-term-care insurance that meet certain Federal standards to be deducted from taxable income. Your premiums can be added to your other deductible medical expenses, and if all of your medical expenses are greater than 7.5 percent of your adjusted gross income (AGI), your premiums will increase your itemized deductions. The maximum premium amount that you can claim increases with age. Moreover, the benefits of tax-qualified policies are also tax-free. Two points seem noteworthy. The first is that, like many deductions, the tax savings may be more apparent than real. For example, a person with an AGI of $50,000 will only be able to deduct the portion of medical expenses that exceed $3,750. Another drawback is that qualified plans may feature more restrictive benefit triggers than nonqualified plans. If you bought a plan prior to January 1, 1997, it is probably tax-qualified because these policies were grandfathered by the 1996 Act.

NAIC Minimum Standards

In an attempt to protect consumers and limit complexity in the long-term-care insurance market, the National Association of Insurance Commissioners (NAIC) has been recommending policy guidelines since the 1980s. In August 2000, NAIC updated its "model regulation" for long-term-care insurance, and as of June 2002, 31 states have adopted or are in the process of adopting this most recent model. Some states have included additional regulations. A review of the model's major provisions should give you a better understanding of long-term-care insurance and the issues to consider when shopping for a policy. According to the NAIC model, all long-term-care insurance policies should provide at least the following:

- Definitions of terms should be stated clearly in the policy. In addition, a complete description of all "covered" providers of services, especially their licensure or certification requirements or degree status, must be included in the contract. A number of policies have failed to pay claims because the care received did not meet the technical definition of "covered" care. For example, policyholders have had benefits withheld because the care provider was not licensed by the state, as required by the policy; still others have had their claims denied because the facility did not meet the company's criteria, which were not stated in the policy.

- All policies must be "guaranteed renewable." That is, you may continue your policy by timely payment of premiums—the insurer cannot decrease coverage or increase premiums on you *individually* due to age or physical condition. However, the insurer may increase premiums over a class of policies, which could include yours. For those on fixed incomes, this could make policies prohibitively expensive.

• Striving to stabilize premiums, NAIC regulations now require insurers to certify the adequacy of their rates using actuarial models. Under the previous regulation, companies were required to use a 60 percent loss-ratio (the ratio of claims to premiums) as a basis to calculate rates for long-term-care insurance policies. For example, an initial 60 percent loss-ratio requirement means that if the claims were expected to be $600, then the premium could not be greater than $1,000 (600/1000 = 0.6). This loss-ratio method artificially limited initial premiums and created an incentive for insurers to increase claims later on so they could raise rates. Under the new amendments, there is no fixed loss-ratio requirement on initial rate filings, but penalties will be imposed in the future if there are substantial rate increases. Some states have enacted additional limits on rate increases.

• To protect policyholders against substantial rate increases, insurers must offer them the option to purchase "nonforfeiture benefits." These benefits are triggered after a lapse or nonpayment on a policy. If the premium increase of a lapsed policy exceeds a certain percentage (based on age) the policyholder may (1) pay the higher premium for the same level of coverage; (2) pay the same premium for a decrease in the level of coverage; or (3) convert the coverage to a paid-up status (no more premiums) with a shortened benefit period. In each of these cases underwriting is prohibited. According to the Health Insurance Association of America, a nonforfeiture benefit can add 20 to 100 percent to a policy's cost.

• Insurers must offer policyholders the option to purchase "inflation protection." This option is crucial because the costs of long-term care are increasing faster than the rate of general price inflation. Thus, the nominal benefits offered by a policy may be woefully inadequate to cover the actual costs of care when it is needed. For instance, a nursing home that cost $153 a day in 2001 (the national average cost for that year) will cost $406 a day in 20 years if nursing home costs rise five percent annually. Most policies with inflation protection automatically increase benefits each year by a fixed compound percentage, usually five percent. If

91

price inflation accelerates, even this "protection" would prove inadequate. In that case, a provision that guarantees to pay a specified percentage of actual charges and has no dollar limit would provide better inflation protection. Some policies provide a guaranteed right to increase benefit levels periodically without providing evidence of insurability. Again, this feature comes at a cost. Inflation protection can boost premiums 40 percent to over 100 percent, depending on the option you select.

- Limitations and exclusions of coverage may be permitted only for preexisting conditions or diseases; mental or nervous disorders, other than Alzheimer's disease or other dementia; alcoholism or drug addiction; illness or injury caused by an act of war, service in the armed forces, attempted suicide, or intentionally self-inflicted injury; services provided in a government facility and for which benefits are available under Medicare or other government program; and services received abroad. Carefully review any exclusions that apply to policies you are considering. Be sure that the definitions of excluded coverage are specific and that you clearly understand them. If you have any questions about what is or is not covered, ask the agent for a clarification *in writing*. If you decide to purchase the policy, any such written documents should be kept with it.

- A group long-term-care policy should be convertible to an individual policy with comparable coverage for a period of 31 days following the discontinuation of group insurance. The policyholder must have been continuously insured under the group plan for at least six months. Most long-term-care policies are sold to individuals, but you can buy group coverage through an employer or through membership in an association. If your employment ends or your employer cancels the group plan, most states require that the converted coverage provide "substantially similar" benefits and premiums.

- No insurer may engage in "post-claims underwriting." Many policyholders have complained of insurance companies reviewing their health histories only *after* a claim had been filed. Insurers have denied claims and refunded the premiums paid into these policies if they deemed the health histories inadequate. To prevent this practice, NAIC requires that a number of provisions be added to the medical history application and that insurers accept such medical histories before or at the time the policy is issued.

- Long-term-care insurance sales representatives are prohibited from making misleading representations; from using high-pressure tactics such as force, fright, or threat, whether explicit or implicit; and from employing "cold-lead advertising," which hides the real purpose of the solicitation—to sell insurance. Agents must review a personal worksheet with each applicant to determine suitability of benefits in each case and whether the applicant will be able to afford the policy if premiums increase or income becomes fixed or decreases. In addition, each applicant must be given NAIC's "Shopper's Guide to Long-term-care insurance." Of course, there will always be pushy salespeople, some of whom may employ shady sales tactics. If any insurance representative says you must "sign right away" or the policy will not be available, walk away. Consider purchasing a policy only after you have had the chance to review its provisions (in private and with the counsel of knowledgeable third parties) and to compare its costs and benefits with a number of other policies.

Though the NAIC model does establish some minimum standards for benefits, it does not prescribe the specific benefits that a long-term policy must offer. Thus, even a policy that claims to adhere to the NAIC model may not provide adequate coverage.

"Low" Early Retirement Premiums: Who Benefits?

Insurers emphasize that long-term care contracts will be unaffordable to most people unless they purchase their policies years before there is a significant probability that care will be required. According to the U.S. General Accounting Office (GAO), in 2001, a person age 79, assuming good health, typically paid about two-and-a-half times more in premiums than a 65 year old and about six to 10 times more than a 50 year old for the same policy. A check of Quotesmith.com reveals that the most expensive policies for a 79-year old can cost $20,000 or more per year, which is presumably beyond the means of many, perhaps most, retired persons. However, the relatively lower premiums at a younger age will be paid over a longer period. Would one be better off financially to invest the pre-

93

mium amounts prudently in a personal investment account instead of paying insurance companies for years?

Take, for example, a representative policy promising unlimited lifetime benefits of $200 per day after a 30-day elimination period. The policy also includes home health care benefits and 5 percent compound inflation protection. Even though the national average cost per day of a nursing home stay in 2001 was $153, we chose a $200 daily benefit because the national average does not include items such as therapies and medications that could significantly increase expenses. Furthermore, nursing home rates vary according to size of accommodations, services available, quality of care, and amenities.

Since the most important function of health-care insurance is to cover the potentially catastrophic tail-end costs, as unlikely as they may be, lifetime benefits appear to be the best option for comparison. Indeed, any sales pitch that exhorts the need for a limited-coverage nursing home policy must ignore the obvious shortcomings of all such policies; namely, that if long-term nursing home care *were* required, say, beginning at age 66, benefits would run out before even age 70.

According to Quotesmith.com, for a 65-year-old male in good health and living in Florida, annual premiums for policies that meet our criteria range from $5,184 to $11,254 from companies rated A+ by *Best Ratings*. Although higher-priced policies presumably have more lenient benefit triggers and coverage restrictions than the lower priced ones, the GAO found that premiums for a similar policy for the same individual can vary widely from company to company. For our example, we chose the least expensive in the above range, a non-smoker tax-qualified policy with annual premiums of $5,184. (For a 50-year-old male, the premiums vary from $2,581 to $5,603.) We assume for the sake of argument that some nursing home care becomes needed at age 85, even though statistics show that at any given time only one in nine men and one in five women age 85 and over are in a nursing home.*

Based on that assumption, the 65-year-old male would pay

---

* All nursing home residency data comes from The National Nursing Home Survey: 1999 summary. National Center for Health Statistics. Vital Health Stat 13(152). 2002.

$103,680 into the policy before entering a home ($5,184 per year for 20 years). Add to that amount the cost of the 30 day elimination period—that is, $15,930 in 20 years assuming nursing home costs continue to rise five percent annually, increasing daily expenses from $200 to $531—and the beneficiary would have to pay $119,610 before the policy begins returning benefits. Thereafter, however, benefits presumably continue for the length of confinement. If the premiums were invested at five percent over the same 20-year period, by age 85 the accrued interest and principal before deducting taxes would total $179,985—the equivalent of 339 nursing home days. (The average length of stay for those discharged from nursing homes was 272 days; 68 percent had lengths of stay that were less than three months.)

Although the national average cost per year of a nursing home stay in 2001 was roughly $56,000, one consideration that is often overlooked is that for a person living alone, the relevant cost of confinement is the cost above and beyond what he would spend if he were not confined. According to the Bureau of Labor Statistic's *Consumer Expenditure Survey*, in 2000, unmarried women age 65 and over spent $18,000 on average, per year. The figure for men was $21,000. The point is that once a person who lives alone enters a nursing home, outlays for housing, food, transportation, entertainment, and the like diminish greatly.

In short, if you paid premiums for 20 years, amounting to tens of thousands of dollars, at the end of that time there still would be only about one chance in five that you would receive *any* benefit (assuming that your illness required skilled nursing home confinements that satisfied the conditions for payment of benefits). On the other hand, if you invest the same amounts in interest-bearing accounts or dividend-yielding securities, by the end of 20 years you would have a sizeable fund to draw on if needed. But again, there would be only about a 20 percent chance that you would have to tap that fund. The much larger probability would be that you would *not* need it. You would be able to pass your private investment fund along to your heirs or, if you are admitted to a home for only several months, by drawing on your own fund you avoid policy triggers and coverage limitations, leaving you greater freedom to arrange your custodial care.

95

However, if your "several months" turns into "many months" or years, these freedoms will probably evaporate as your fund runs dry. Although the probability of such a lengthy confinement is quite small for any randomly chosen individual, the actual risk is much smaller than the sellers of these policies would have you believe. Your own decision will depend largely on your personal and family health history and family circumstances.

Will You Need Nursing Home Care?

Most of the literature sent out by insurance companies to promote their policies may exaggerate the probability that any individual will require long-term nursing home care. One statistic widely cited is that "one of every two people over age 65 will require some form of long-term care." (Despite its widespread use in brochures, websites, and periodicals, we have not been able to track down the statistic's source.) Although statements like this may frighten some people into buying a policy, far fewer Americans are confined for as many years in nursing homes as an insurance salesman would have you believe.

Surveys of nursing home utilization by the Department of Health and Human Services' National Center for Health Statistics (NCHS) have generally been regarded as the most accurate measures to date of the long-term care risks of the elderly. The NCHS's latest National Nursing Home Survey (1999) provides estimates of nursing home facilities, current residents, and discharges. Perhaps the most explosive statistics to come out of the NCHS are that about two in five persons over age 65 will require nursing home care at some time in their lives and that, on average, those now in nursing homes have been confined for nearly two and a half years. Taken together, these statistics have been cited by healthcare activists and insurance salespeople alike as evidence that the elderly face a very substantial risk of confinement for many years in a nursing home.

Such a conclusion is unwarranted. Even though as many as 40 percent of today's elderly *may* at some time require care in a nursing home, the overwhelming number of nursing home admissions result in short stays. The latest NCHS survey of discharges, which includes patients that died, shows that more than two-thirds of all discharges (68.3 percent) were for stays of less than three months, and slightly more than four-fifths (83.2 percent) of all discharged patients had

96

been confined for under a year. Indeed, patients who had been confined for three years or longer represented only 7.4 percent of all discharges. The average length of stay was 272 days.

What accounts for the seeming discrepancy between these two sets of data? The NCHS survey of nursing home residents is based on a *population* census. A census counts only those who reside at a given place at the time the census is taken. It says nothing about those who may have lived there previously or about those who will live there at some future time. Because short-term residents are less likely to be on the nursing home rolls on a given night, they are less likely to be counted. Thus, the sample of residents is more likely to contain long-term nursing home patients and, conversely, to underestimate short nursing home stays.

The following example illustrates why. Assume that a nursing home with 50 beds initially admits patients with a wide range of clinical problems. Of those initial 50, say, 20 die within a few weeks of admission and 25 return home, leaving five still in residence and 45 beds available. Of the 45 "new" patients, assume that 20 die and 20 go home—but five remain, enlarging the number of long-term residents to 10 and leaving only 40 beds available. The process continues until most beds are occupied by long-term patients. Unless an institution specifically reserves a percentage of its beds for "transients," over time almost all beds in a given facility will become occupied by long-term patients. The NCHS nursing home population censuses confirm this circumstance, yet reveal nothing about the experiences of the vastly greater number of patients who were discharged after short stays, or about those who never were admitted to a nursing home at all.

The NCHS survey of nursing home discharges, on the other hand, is designed to provide information on completed episodes of care during the year and reflect a rough record of the "flow" of patients in and out of institutions. Although it is far from clear that the available discharge data are representative of the "average" nursing home experience of the elderly (if there is such a thing), discharges plainly indicate that the risks of long-term confinement have been far less than might be inferred from the NCHS survey of nursing home residents.

Overall, 1.5 million seniors—about 4.3 percent of the U.S. population age 65 and older—resided in nursing homes in 1999. The likelihood that either spouse will require long-term care during the early years of retirement is very slight. In 1999, only 1.1 percent of men and women aged 65-74 years were confined in a nursing home. Among *married* persons aged 65-74, nursing home residency rates were minuscule: around 0.2 percent of the population in that age group.

The chances that nursing home care will be needed increase markedly with age. Of those aged 75-84 years, about 3.1 percent of men and 5.1 percent of women were receiving long-term care. However, nursing home residency jumps sharply among those 85 years and older. Of those elderly, about 1 in 9 men and 1 in 5 women resided in nursing homes in 1999.

Among residents, nearly three-fourths were women and one half were 85 and older. Unmarried patients outnumber married ones by almost nine to one. The incidence of nursing home confinement for unmarried men over 65 is about twice the incidence for married men over 65, but the former are outnumbered by unmarried women four to one. Indeed, unmarried (single or widowed) women constitute by far the largest category of long-term care patients, comprising almost two-thirds of the resident population.

The characteristics of current long-term nursing home residents tend to be far more specific than might be implied by popular discussions of the long-term-care "crisis." Although many of the elderly may have one or more physical conditions that prevent them from being totally independent, this does not necessarily mean that they all will end up in nursing homes. According to government statistics, nearly one-seventh of the nation's elders—an estimated 5.2 million—have a limitation in either one or more activites of daily living (such as preparing food, housekeeping, and handling finances). However, nearly 80 percent of them live at home or in community-base settings such as assisted-living facilities. Informal, unpaid caregivers such as a spouse, children, relatives, friends or volunteers provide the majority of the care. This experience applies especially to elderly married men, who often are cared for by wives who can be expected, in statistical terms, to outlive them. Clearly, most older people with disabilities can manage in noninstitutional settings.

In short, most nursing home admissions that result in long-term stays would seem to be those of aged unmarried men and women—mostly women—without family or friends to care for them, usually because mental impairment and associated behavioral problems have made them dangerous to themselves or difficult to care for.

Only the "Hale and Hearty" Need Apply

Unfortunately, if you are in a high-risk category that might justify an "investment" in a long-term-care policy, you may not be able to obtain one. To screen out high risks, insurers reject virtually any applicant they think is likely to make a claim. In this regard, these policies have changed little since their inception. Unlike life insurers, who are concerned with your risk of dying, long-term-care insurers focus on your risk of needing care. Thus, they might consider a person with a history of cancer to be a better risk than someone who uses a four-pronged cane.

A key part of the screening process is the applicant interview when an examiner comes to your home to evaluate your physical and mental condition. Examiners evaluate your mobility and survey your ability to do basic activites such as bathing, toileting, dressing, and getting in and out of a chair. They also conduct various cognitive tests, such as word memory games and asking you to count backward by threes. More subtly, the interviewers observe your demeanor, grooming, and living environment, looking for any indication of memory loss, confusion, or lack of mobility. They may ask to see your driver's license, not for identification purposes but because maintaining a license is a sign of mobility. They may ask you to show what prescriptions you are taking, partly to see if you have trouble remembering them.

You cannot avoid these tests; refusing to cooperate would be an automatic disqualifier. In the book *J.K. Lasser's Choosing the Right Long-Term-Care Insurance*, Benjamin Lipson suggests ways to improve your performance. For example, schedule the interview at your best time of day, gather all your prescription bottles beforehand, and clean the house. Avoid making jokes to your doctors about "senior moments" because that might show up in the medical notes they must provide to the insurance company. (See page 105 for more information on Lipson's book.)

As already discussed, insurers also try to control their risks by carefully defining the conditions under which they will pay benefits and by promising to pay only a fixed amount for, in many cases, a limited period. Companies have developed these tight controls on long-term-care policies, in combination with high and seemingly arbitrary premiums, because the pool of high-risk insureds is relatively small and the insurers' loss experiences are very limited. Max E. Lemberger proposed early on ("A New Deal for Long-Term Care," *Best's Review,* October 1987) that long-term-care policies ought to be designed to cover a wide range of risks that embrace not only the possible need for nursing home care but also the various degrees of "disability" that result from aging, thus protecting policyholders against a much broader range of losses for longer periods. His point was that the "risk pool" must be broadened very substantially if long-term-care insurance is to be made affordable and practical to most persons.

Insurers are beginning to address this problem. Most long-term-care policies now pay for home health care, either as a basic benefit or an additional rider available for a higher premium, although the benefit is normally a fraction (generally half) of the daily benefit for nursing home confinement. On the surface, this should substantially increase the pool of high-risk insureds since almost 80 percent of long-term care is given in a community setting. However, even a top policy, it should be noted, may not keep you out of a nursing home. The health conditions that trigger benefits for this care usually are not the mild impairments that lead many elderly to get help with cooking, house cleaning, and shopping in order to help them maintain independent lifestyles. Rather, home care benefits usually become available only under the same restrictive conditions that are used to qualify for nursing home benefits.

The problem is that individuals who require this much care probably need round-the-clock assistance or supervision. But full-time paid care costs even more at home than it does at a nursing home, and most policies pay benefits sufficient to cover only a few hours of care per day. Some policies require that care be provided only by licensed caregivers, who usually charge more, which further limits the amount of care that can be purchased. This may be adequate if the insured can rely on a strong network of family and friends to provide care the rest of the time, every day. Otherwise, there would be too many gaps to fill.

Long-Term Care (Living Benefits) Life Insurance

The life insurance industry has also attempted to expand the risk pool by developing new "long-term care" life insurance products. A growing number of insurers now offer policyholders the option of taking their death benefits from life insurance policies *before* they die. This innovation was introduced in the United States in response to AIDS patients seeking additional financial resources to help cover medical costs. Since then, this provision has been expanded to cover most terminal illnesses and many catastrophic illnesses as well. The option is available in new policies or as a rider to existing ones.

The logic behind offering "living benefits" is simple. The insurance company eventually will have to pay death benefits to a terminally ill policyholder's beneficiary, and it makes little difference if they pay it slightly sooner rather than later. The cost to the insurer is minimal, representing only the potential interest earnings lost on the benefit when it is paid out, say, a year earlier. Insurers can make up this cost by paying a living benefit that is somewhat less than the face value of the policy. For the insured, accelerated benefits can help defray medical costs and reduce the financial upheaval that can follow even an expected death. Moreover, the insured could conceivably use the funds to finance lifesaving medical treatment.

The most conservative policies provide early death benefits only in the case of terminal illness. The living benefit is a percentage of the face value of the policy, typically ranging from 50 to 80 percent. Some insurers also offer accelerated benefits to cover long-term care or confinement in a nursing home, regardless of whether the patient is terminally ill. In these cases, the insured may be allowed to choose a monthly benefit rather than a lump sum. The monthly benefit is usually a percentage of the face value. For example, a $150,000 policy might pay two percent of the face value, or $3,000, per month. Since the fixed amount does not vary with the cost of care, the living benefit is similar to a hospital indemnity policy. Whether the insured chooses a lump sum or monthly benefits, he can elect the living benefits option only once, and the consent of the beneficiary may be required.

Policy provisions vary widely among companies. For example, some pay long-term "catastrophic" benefits only after the insured has been confined to a nursing home for three or even six months.

Others pay these monthly benefits only if the insured is hospitalized prior to confinement in a nursing home (most nursing home residents do not require hospitalization). Others restrict the types of illnesses that qualify for benefits. The broadest coverage includes heart disease, life-threatening cancer, stroke, Alzheimer's disease, kidney failure, and liver failure. Most cover any illness that leaves the insured with a life expectancy of 12 months or less, although even this provision may vary among policies. Every diagnosis requires verification by a doctor. In addition to differences in coverage, the percentage of the face value paid in advance also varies from company to company.

The Health Insurance Portability and Accountability Act of 1996 eliminates the income tax on certain advanced payments of life insurance, including accelerated death benefits under a standard life insurance policy. For payments to avoid taxation, a chronically ill person must be certified by a licensed health care practitioner to be unable to perform at least two of six activities of daily living for at least 90 days. Persons who need to be supervised to protect their personal health or safety (*e.g.*, Alzheimer's patients) also fall under the standard. Accelerated benefit payments are only treated as tax-free if they are paid under a rider or other contractual agreement as they would be under a long-term-care insurance policy. The payments are not tax-free if an insured's long-term care is already being paid for by long-term-care insurance or Medicaid. Consult a tax attorney or accountant for more specific advice on this tax issue.

Older people who might otherwise let their life insurance lapse (say, because their children have grown) might instead choose to keep it in force to take advantage of the availability of tax-free accelerated benefits. The cost of this simple rider is minimal, and some companies provide it at no extra charge. However, living benefits are not costless. The death benefit, the cash value, and the loan value of the policy all will be reduced if the insured takes advantage of the early benefits option. Most important, remember that the living benefits provided by a life insurance policy are no substitute for a comprehensive health insurance policy.

Nursing Homes In Perspective

The nursing home is a relatively modern creation that evolved mainly as a result of two concurrent developments: the advent of modern antibiotics that increased life expectancies remarkably, and increased "middle class" affluence that followed World War II. Prior to that time, care for the elderly infirm usually was provided either through family or through numerous voluntary organizations, charities, and churches that sponsored "old folks homes." In most cases, the burden of such care probably was less than might be imagined today. Most elderly people who subsequently contracted serious illnesses—pneumonia or some other infectious disease—died, and the caregiver was relieved of further responsibility. By contrast, postwar medical advances, most notably antibiotics and other drugs, kept such people alive but often in physical circumstances that did not permit them to live independently. A parent might recover from a serious illness and require more care than ever. The absence of support services to help family caregivers, the nursing home provided an increasingly efficient solution.

More recent progress in medical technology (artificial joints, bypass surgery, organ transplants, drug therapy, eye surgery, and the like) may be reversing that trend by enabling many older people whose conditions formerly would have made them nursing home candidates to continue to "manage" their own lives. With increasing availability of home care services, a primary concern of many elderly with disabilities may not be how long they will be confined in a nursing home, but rather how best to manage the many other services that are available to them. The period of absolute dependency, when institutionalization may be necessary, seems very likely to shrink—possibly dramatically.

Trends in nursing home usage suggest that older persons may already be living in the community longer and entering nursing homes later and sicker than before. Options such as home health care, assisted living, and continuing care retirement communities are helping to drive this trend. Visiting nurses, hospice care, physical therapy, respite care, and other community resources aid informal caregivers, allowing the elderly to remain home longer.

Unless the number of new beds grows markedly, an aging population may increasingly limit *long-term* nursing home space to those with the greatest dependencies, mostly the chronically mentally ill. Nursing homes may in effect become surrogate mental institutions— a process that to some extent probably already has been accelerated by the deinstitutionalization of mental patients—while long-term care for the remaining elderly is routinely provided by other means.

What Should You Do?

Long-term-care insurance, as currently marketed, remains confusing. The cost of long-term-care policies varies greatly, and it is often unclear why. In addition, consumers must struggle to understand and to be able to compare how benefits are paid, what services are covered, where services are covered, what is not covered, when and why benefits are triggered, and so forth. Although the policies may be less deceptive than they were a decade ago, they remain very confusing, making it difficult to know whether a policy is providing adequate protection.

Assuming you can decipher the fine print of the policy, you also have to be able to pay for it. Comprehensive long-term-care contracts remain among the most expensive insurance products on the market. Affordability is even more of an issue for married couples, since spouses must purchase individual coverage. (To reduce this financial burden a bit, some insurers offer discounts to married couples when both purchase long-term care coverage.) Many prospective buyers will not be able to afford an adequate policy. They will be tempted to buy a cheaper policy whose benefits are too small or too limited to do much good. You should not buy a policy if you cannot afford the premiums or are not reasonably sure you can pay the premium for the rest of your life or until you need care.

In shopping for a policy, do your homework ahead of time; don't expect to get unbiased, accurate, and comprehensive information from an agent. One useful source is the "Shopper's Guide to Long-term-care insurance," available free on request from the National Association of Insurance Commissioners, 2301 McGee, Suite 800, Kansas City, Missouri 64108-2604, (816) 842-3600, website at www.naic.org. Also, check with your state Insurance Department (listed in Chapter VII) for additional publications that may be available in your state. Some states require the Insurance Commissioner to prepare annually a consumer rate guide for long-term-care insurance. These guides may include a list of companies selling in your state, the types of benefits and policies you can buy, and a rate history of each company.

In addition, *J. K. Lasser's Choosing the Right Long-Term Care Insurance,* by Benjamin Lipson (John Wiley and Sons, 2002, $16.95 softcover), is a very readable and complete guide to purchasing long-term care insurance. Lipson, an independent insurance broker, describes how these policies work, what services are covered, how benefits are paid, and what to expect when you apply for a policy. He includes many real-life examples and practical advice, from "a list of questions insurance companies hope you never ask" to "finding a seller you can trust."

Also, get as much information as you can about the long-term care services and facilities you might use, including quality of care and how much they charge. When you are ready to begin investigating individual policies, check with several companies and agents. Be sure to compare benefits, the limits on your coverage, any exclusions, and premiums. Review the companies' rate increase histories. Choose only a financially sound insurance company.

Be sure you accurately complete your application. Your medical history is important. If the information is not accurate and complete and the insurer used the information to issue you the policy, the company can refuse to pay your claims and can even cancel your policy.

Whether you should buy a long-term-care insurance policy will depend largely on your age, health history, overall retirement goals, family situation, income and assets, and the types of services and policies available in your area. After doing your investigating, you may decide not to buy a policy. But at least you will be making an informed decision and will have a better idea of what to consider if you want to make alternative arrangements for care.

X.

LONG-TERM CARE ALTERNATIVES

P RESUMABLY, most of us would rather spend our final years in home surroundings of our own choosing rather than in an institutionalized setting that is forced on us. As discussed in the preceding chapter, the possibility that you will reside many years in a nursing home is quite small. Statistically, the vast majority of elderly Americans live out their lives in their own or in family members' homes, or in some other type of community setting.

This does not mean that many older people will never require assistance, perhaps substantial assistance, with their living arrangements, or decide to move to more convenient homes. Fortunately, a variety of alternatives to nursing homes are becoming increasingly available. Developments in medicine, support services, and demographics almost guarantee that the market for long-term care will continue to change. It remains to be seen if all the options will succeed.

In this chapter, we discuss three options—assisted living communities, continuing care retirement communities (CCRCs), and home health and elder care—that have become widely used alternatives to conventional nursing home care.

Assisted Living Communities

Assisted living communities have proliferated in recent years, and currently more than six million Americans live in some 20,000 such residences.

Ideally, assisted living allows persons who can no longer live by themselves, but who do not need 24-hour a day care, to receive help with daily routines in a homelike setting while supposedly encouraging maximum independence. Residences are generally private rentals, varying in size from one-room efficiencies to full apartments in structures ranging from converted homes to high-rise apartment complexes. Depending on the facility, amenities may include housekeeping, 24-hour security and staff availability, emergency call buttons in each unit, daily room checks, specially prepared foods, three meals a day served in a common dining room, laundry service, transportation, and even social and recreational activities and exercise programs.

On-site nursing services and assistance with activities of daily living—such as bathing, dressing, walking, medication reminders, and meals—are based on an individual's needs. In some facilities the basic fee covers all services. In others, the basic fee covers only limited services with additional charges for services on an as-needed basis. This may partly account for the wide range in daily rates, which vary, approximately, from $15 to $200 nationwide. It is important, therefore, when comparing assisted living arrangements, to ask what is included in the basic rate and what services are available for extra charges. For example, are the services provided by the facility's employees or through other agencies? If you need additional assistance later on, will you have to move? In many states, residents can be dismissed with 30 days notice when their personal care or medical needs exceed the facility's ability or willingness to provide it.

There are some indications that this approach—a largely untested and unregulated industry—is running into problems. According to recent news reports, developers have overestimated demand for these centers and have overbuilt. Occupancy rates have leveled off, and operators are under pressure to cut costs and to attract new occupants. The lack of uniform standards forces consumers shopping for assisted living to rely primarily on providers for information. Assisted living facilities are often marketed more like real estate than care. The national Eldercare Locator (1-800-677-1116) provides the phone number of the appropriate local long-term care ombudsman, who will inform you if any complaints have been filed and whether they have been resolved.

For more information about assisted living, including how to choose a facility, contact the Assisted Living Federation of America, 10300 Eaton Place, Suite 400, Fairfax, VA 22030. Tel: (703) 691-8100; www.alfa.org. Also, contact the Consumer Consortium on Assisted Living, 2342 Oak Street, Falls Church, VA 22046. Tel: (703) 533-8121; www.ccal.org.

Continuing Care Retirement Communities

Continuing care contracts, sometimes called life care contracts, are offered by more than 1,100 continuing care retirement communities (CCRCs) throughout the United States. These communities provide access to a continuum of care and living arrangements on one campus, from apartments or homes for independent seniors to assisted living and nursing facilities. Most people choose to move in when they are still healthy; the average age at entrance is about 75 years. Accommodations among CCRCs vary widely—from luxury suites or bungalows to modest studios—as do the communities' related amenities. Some have auditoriums, tennis courts and swimming pools, elaborate recreation centers, libraries, shopping facilities, movie theaters, and the like on the premises. Often, planned outings and other activities are an integral part of CCRC life. Those who are able may still travel and enjoy life outside the community.

CCRCs promise to provide whatever care you may require throughout your life in a setting appropriate for that level of assistance, and both you and your spouse can live without worrying about "what comes next." You know what facilities you will occupy if you become unable to manage for yourselves. If it becomes necessary, the staff may prepare meals (available for home delivery or in a common dining room), provide housekeeping services and emergency help, and offer custodial or nursing care on a regular basis while you continue to live in an independent setting. And you have the comfort and convenience of living "together" in the community even though one spouse may require full-time nursing care; nursing facilities usually are available on the premises and the non-institutionalized spouse may remain in the apartment. Often, nursing care arrangements proceed flexibly, for example, with daily or weekend visits "home." Or if the need for nursing care ceases, say, after convalescence from surgery, the patient simply returns to his or her apartment (unless the institutionalization of a surviving spouse is terminal).

CCRCs probably are not for everyone. Even though they permit independent living for as long as possible, most such communities cannot avoid an "institutional atmosphere." To some extent, this is intentional—and may be in the interest of most residents. Although residents are free to do as they wish, they are encouraged to participate in community activities as a means of enriching their lives. For many older people, this is a desirable feature, while for others it may not be.

Not surprisingly, CCRCs are relatively expensive. Generally, they require a one-time entrance fee and monthly payments thereafter. (In some cases, residents purchase a condominium or cooperative unit instead of paying an initial fee.) Entrance fees vary from lows of $20,000 to highs of $400,000 depending on the CCRC and on the type of living unit, which can range from a studio or "alcove" apartment (one room with scaled-down kitchen and bath) to luxury two-bedroom suites, cluster homes, and even single-family homes.

You usually pay the entrance fee in a lump sum when you sign the continuing care contract, which is the legal agreement that secures your accommodations and services over the long term. Refund policies vary by community and by when you leave (before the contract expires, on death, or after the contract ends). Some communities pay full refunds, while others treat the entrance fee as a nonrefundable "gift;" some refund a percentage of the fees (up to 90 percent) regardless of when or how you leave, while others decrease the refund the longer you stay.

In addition to the entrance fee, current residents can expect to pay from about $450 per month for a low cost CCRC in Oklahoma to about $4,000 per month for a high-cost community in California, or around $5,000 to $50,000 per year in monthly maintenance charges. For most residents, monthly fees fall between these extremes—from $1,250 to $2,500, or between $15,000 and $30,000 per year. In addition, residents must have Medicare and pay for supplemental insurance coverage since CCRCs do not pay for medical bills.

Both the entrance fee and the monthly maintenance fee will vary depending on the type of contract you sign. The more services the contract covers, the more costly it will be. Continuing care contracts generally fall into one of the three categories described below.

All-Inclusive Plans provide, as needed, all the services offered by the CCRC. *Residential services* usually include apartment cleaning and maintenance, dining room service, flat linen laundry service, grounds maintenance, kitchen appliances, personal laundry facilities, dietetic services, use of scheduled transportation, storage, tray service, and utilities. *Health-related services* usually include an emergency call system, home health care in your apartment, long-term nursing care, recreational therapy, and social services. With these plans, your total costs are predictable—but only if the contract pro-

110

hibits or limits inflation adjustments.

Modified Plans usually provide some of the residential services listed above and require an additional fee for other services. They also provide only a *specified amount* of long-term nursing care. If you exceed that amount, you pay an additional charge. Home health care usually is not included in modified plans and additional fees are charged for it.

Fee-for-Service Plans generally provide an independent living unit, limited residential services, and guarantees *access to* nursing care. It does not, however, pay for nursing care; residents must pay full per diem charges, when required.

What You See Now May Not be What You Get Later

Will the community you committed your bank account and life to be there when you most need it? CCRCs may leave you little flexibility to alter arrangements once you have moved in, and many residents may have to share its fate. If its financial health fades and food service starts serving "mystery meals" seven days a week, the attendants become less-attentive than at first, and the buildings and grounds and security arrangements deteriorate, you may be stuck, depending on your contract and circumstances. This situation differs from services that you purchase independently. Those you can change if they are not doing a satisfactory job.

As residents age and require more services, a CCRC's finances and resources are likely to be strained. Thus it may not be prudent to enter a "new" community with a large population of relatively young healthy adults—no matter how appealing. The facility could deteriorate dramatically as the fit become unfit. On the other hand, if a community with a more "mature" population is handling the needs of those people well, and its finances remain sound, then it may be expected to provide you with quality services in the future.

Thus, if you think a CCRC may be right for you, shop around and start looking early. The waiting lists for entrance into the most desirable communities may be as long as 10 years. The best way to determine if a facility is well-managed is to visit it. Talk to the residents. Are they satisfied with the services? Is the food good? Has there been any deterioration in the physical facilities or in the "extras"? Most important, obtain copies of the organization's financial statements and review them with your accountant. If they are unsatisfactory or leave unanswered questions, look elsewhere. Finally, buy only a contract that offers a substantial refund at *any* time during its life.

Most state insurance departments, listed in Chapter VII, have published free guides to these facilities. Other useful publications are *The Continuing Care Retirement Community: A Guidebook for Consumers* and the *Consumers' Directory of Continuing Care Retirement Communities,* both available from the American Association of Homes and Services for the Aging (AAHSA), 2519 Connecticut Avenue NW, Washington, D.C. 20008-1520; phone 202-783-2242; www.aahsa.org. The Continuing Care Accreditation Commission establishes standards for CCRC quality and provides consumers with information and a list of accredited communities. For more information, contact the commission at 2519 Connecticut Avenue NW, Washington, D.C. 20008-1520; phone 202-783-7286; www.ccaconline.org.

After you have determined costs and living conditions of a number of retirement communities, you will be in a better position to compare those costs and services with the costs and services that might be obtained elsewhere and that would permit you and your spouse to continue to live in a noninstitutional setting—namely, your own home.

Home Health and Elder Care

Presumably, most of us would prefer to remain at home even though we may require assistance of some form—housekeeping services, personal services, health care, or whatever. In fact, many of the services that are provided by nursing homes now are available on a home-care basis from independent contractors and a variety of community and religious groups. Some services are covered by Medicare or Medicaid and many operate on a nonprofit basis or are subsidized by local agencies for the aging. Some are provided free of charge.

Home health care services include skilled nursing care, custodial nursing care, home therapy, and clinical testing services (*e.g.*, routine blood tests can be performed by a health care technician in your own home, saving a trip to the doctor's office or clinic). Many local elder care agencies provide low cost or free transportation for senior citizens, volunteer housekeeping services, live-in companion referrals, "meals on wheels" food services, shopping services, and the like.

Also, families caring for loved ones can get rest and time off through services such as adult day care and respite care. And today, so-called life-call communications services are widely available to homebound seniors for a relatively modest fee, providing help at the press of a button in case of a personal or medical emergency.

Your Own "Life-Care" Home?

Especially in view of the Medicaid exemption of assets held in the home, it may be possible for many elderly persons to create their own "life-care" home by altering the structure of their house to accommodate walkers or wheelchairs or by adding a "companion's quarters" and utilizing the many home-health and elder care services now available. Of course, this requires planning ahead and major expenditures. But if a comparison of the costs and benefits of home care with the major alternatives, such as nursing homes and continuing care retirement communities, reveals substantial potential savings, you may be better off to consider a home-care plan of your own design.

There are thousands of elder care services in localities across the United States. Your local Yellow Pages may contain listings under "Home Health Services" and "Senior Citizens' Service Organizations" that can direct you to local care providers. The accompanying "Directory of State Aging and Adult Protective Service Agencies" lists offices that can provide you with further information. In addition to the offices listed there, you can find the location and telephone number of the National Association of Area Agencies on Aging (or "N4A") affiliate nearest you by calling the toll-free telephone number for NAAAA's Eldercare Locator 1-800-677-1116 or on the web at www.eldercare.gov. Complete information on the NAAA's 4,800 agencies nationwide is available. You may write to the National Association of Area Agencies on Aging at 927 15th St. NW, 6th Floor, Washington, D.C. 20005. Information is also available from the Federal Administration on Aging, 330 Independence Ave., SW, Washington, DC 20201; 202-619-7501; www.aoa.dhhs.gov.

DIRECTORY OF STATE AGING AND ADULT PROTECTIVE SERVICE AGENCIES

Alabama

Department of Senior Services .... (334) 242-5743
770 Washington Ave., Suite 470, P. O. Box 301851, Montgomery, AL 36130-1851

Adult Services Division .... (205) 242-1350
Dept. of Human Resources, S. Gordon Persons Bldg., 50 Ripley St., Montgomery, AL 36130

Alaska

Commission on Aging .... (907) 269-3250
P. O. Box 110209, Juneau, AK 99811-0209

Adult Services Program .... (907) 465-2145
Division of Family & Young Services, Dept. of Health & Social Services, Pouch H-05, Juneau, AK 99811-0630

Arizona

Aging and Adult Administration .... (602) 542-4446
1789 W. Jefferson St., #950A, Phoenix, AZ 85007

Arkansas

Division of Aging and Adult Servives .... (501) 682-8155
1417 Donaghey Plaza South, P. O. Box 1437/Slot S-530, Little Rock, AR 72203-1437

California

Department of Aging .... (916) 322-5290
1600 K St., Sacramento, CA 85814

Adult Services Bureau .... (916) 322-632
Adult & Family Services Division, Dept. of Social Services, 744 P St., Room 692, Sacramento, CA 95814

Colorado

Aging & Adult Services .... (303) 866-2800
1575 Sherman St., Ground Floor, Denver CO 80203

Connecticut

Division of Elderly Services .... (860) 424-5298
25 Sigourney St., 10th Floor, Hartford CT 06106-5033

Delaware

Services for Aging .... (302) 577-4791
Dept. of Health & Social Services, 1901 N. DuPont Hwy., New Castle, DE 19720

District of Columbia

Office on Aging .... (202) 724-5622
One Judiciary Square, 441 4th St., N.W., 9th Fl., Washington, D.C. 20001

Family Services Administration .... (202) 727-0113
Commission on Social Services, Dept. of Human Services, Randall Bldg., 1st & Eye Sts., S.W., Washington, D.C. 20024

Florida

Department of Elder Affairs .... (850) 414-2000
4040 Esplanade Way, Bldg. B, Suite 152, Tallahassee, FL 32399-0700

Elder Abuse Hotline .... In-State: (800) 96-ABUSE

Georgia

Division of Aging Services .... (404) 657-5258
Dept. of Human Resources, 2 Peachtree St., 36-385
Room 18.403, Atlanta GA 30303

Adult Services Unit .... (404) 894-4440
Social Services Section, Division of Family & Children Services, Dept. of Human Resources, 878 Peachtree St., N.E., Suite 503, Atlanta, GA 30309

Guam

Division of Senior Citizens 011 (671) 475-0263
Dept. of Public Health & Social Services, Government of Guam, Post Office Box 2816, Agana, GU 96910

Hawaii

Executive Office on Aging .... (808) 586-0100
250 S. Hotel St., Suite 109, 4th Floor, Honolulu, HI 96813-2381

Adult Services .... (808) 548-5902
Dept. of Human Services, P. O. Box 339, Honolulu, HI 96809

Idaho

Commission on Aging .... (208) 334-3833
3880 Americana Terr., Ste.120, Boise, ID 83706

Social Services .... (208) 334-5702
Division of Family & Children's Services, Dept. of Health & Welfare, 450 W. State St., 10th Fl., Boise, ID 83720

Illinois

Department on Aging .... (217) 785-3356
421 E. Capitol Ave., #100, Springfield, IL 62701-1789

Indiana

Bureau of Aging and In-Home Services .... (317) 232-7020
402 W. Washington St., P. O. Box 7083, Indianapolis, IN 46207-7083

Adult Protective Services Program .... (317) 232-1750
Adult Services Division, Dept. of Human Services, 251 N. Illinois St., P. O. Box 7083, Indianapolis, IN 46207-7083

Adult Abuse Hotline .... In-State: (800) 992-6978

Iowa

Department of Elder Affairs .... (515) 242-3333
200 10th St., 3rd Fl., Des Moines, IA 50309-3609

Adilt Services .... (515) 281-6129
Bureau of Adult, Children, & Family Services, Dept. of Human Services, Hoover Bldg., 5th Fl., Des Moines, IA 50319

Kansas

Department on Aging .... (785) 296-4986
503 S. Kansas Ave., New England Bldg., Topeka, KS 66603-3404

Commission on Adult Services .... (913) 296-4300
Dept. of Social & Rehabilitative Services, 300 S.W. Oakley, West Hall, Topeka, KS 66606

Kentucky

Office of Aging Services .... (502) 564-6930
Cabinet for Familes & Children, 275 E. Main St., Frankfort, KY 40621

Adult Services .... (502) 564-7043
Division of Family Services, Dept. for Social Services, Cabinet for Human Resources, 275 E. Main St., Frankfort, KY 40621

115

Louisiana

Governor's Office of Elderly Affairs .... (225) 342-7100
4550 N. Boulevard, 2nd Fl., P. O. Box 80374, Baton Rouge, LA 70806-0374

Maine

Bureau of Elder & Adult Services .... (207) 624-5335
35 Anthony Ave., State House Station #11, Augusta, ME 04333-0011

Maryland

Department of Aging .... (410) 767-1100
301 W. Preston St., Room 1007, Baltimore, MD 21201

Adult Protective Services .... (301) 333-0156
Dept. of Human Resources, 311 W. Saratoga St., Baltimore, MD 21201

Massachusetts

Executive Office of Elder Affairs .... (617) 727-7750
One Ashburton Place, 5th Fl., Boston, MA 02108

Elder Abuse Hotline .... In-State: (800) 922-2275-2374

Michigan

Office of Services to the Aging .... (517) 373-8230
611 W. Ottawa St., P. O. Box 30676, Lansing, MI 48909

Adult Services Administration .... (517) 373-2869
Dept. of Social Services, 300 S. Capitol Ave., P. O. Box 30037, Lansing, MI 48909

Minnesota

Board on Aging .... (651) 296-2770
Human Services Bldg., 444 Lafayette Road, St. Paul, MN 55155-3843

Mississippi

Division of Aging & Adult Services .... (601) 359-4925
750 North State St., Jackson, MS 39202

Protection Division .... (601) 354-6644
Bureau of Family and Children's Services, Dept. of Public Welfare, P. O. Box 352, Jackson, MS 39205

Missouri

Division of Senior Services .... (573) 751-3082
615 Howertan Court, Jefferson City, MO 65102-1337

Elder Abuse/Neglect Hotline .... In-State: (800) 392-0210

Montana

Senior & Long Term Care Division .... (406) 444-4077
111 North Sanders, P.O. Box 4210, Helena, MT 59620

Adult Protective Services .... (406) 444-4077
Program Bureau, Program and Planning Division, Dept. of Family Services, P. O. Box 8005, Helena, MT 59604

Nebraska

Division on Aging .... (402) 471-2307
1343 M St., P.O. Box 95044, Lincoln, NE 68509-5044

Nebraska (continued)

Special Services for Children & Adults .... (402) 471-9345
Medical Services Division, Dept. of Social Services, P. O. Box 95026, 301 Centennial Mall-South, 5th Fl., Lincoln, NE 68509-5026

Nevada

Division for Aging Services .... (775) 687-4210
Dept. of Human Resources, 3416 Goni Rd., Bldg. D-132, Carson City, NV 89706

Social Services .... (775) 687-4128
State Welfare Division, Dept. of Human Resources, Capitol Complex, 2527 N. Carson, Carson City, NV 89710

New Hampshire

Division of Elderly & Adult Services .... (603) 271-4680
Dept. of Health & Human Services, State Office Park South, 129 Pleasant St., Bldg.. #1, Concord, NH 03301

New Jersey

Division of Senior Affairs .... (609) 943-3436
Dept. of Health & Human Services, P.O. Box 807, Trenton, NJ 08625-0807

Adult Protective Services .... (609) 292-6726
Division of Youth & Family Services, Dept. of Human Services, 1 S. Montgomery St., CN 717, Trenton, NJ 08625

New Mexico

State Agency on Aging .... (505) 827-7640
La Villa Rivera Bldg., 228 E. Palace Ave., Santa Fe, NM 87501

Adult Services Bureau .... (800) 432-6217
Social Services Division, Human Services Dept., P. O. Box 2348, Pollon Bldg., Santa Fe, NM 87504-2348

New York

State Office for the Aging .... (518) 474-5731
2 Empire State Plaza, Albany, NY 12223-1251

Division of Adult Services .... (518) 432-2974
Dept. of Social Services, 40 N. Pearl St., Albany, NY 12243

North Carolina

Division of Aging .... (919) 733-3983
2101 Mail Serv. Ctr., Raleigh, NC 27699-2101

Adult Protective Services Program .... (919) 733-3818
Division of Social Services, Adult & Family Services, Dept. of Human Resources, 325 N. Salisbury St., Raleigh, NC 27611

North Dakota

Aging Services Division .... (701) 328-8910
Dept. of Human Services, 600 South 2nd St., Ste. 1C, Bismarck, ND 58504

Northern Mariana Islands

CNMI Office on Aging .... (670) 233-1320/1321
P.O. Box 2178, Saipan, MP Northern Mariana Islands 96950

Ohio

Department of Aging .... (614) 466-5500
50 West Broad St., 9th Fl., Columbus, OH 43215-5928

Bureau of Adult Services .... (614) 466-9596
Division of Adult & Child Care Services, Family, Children, & Adult Services, Dept. of Human Services, 30 E. Broad St., Columbus, OH 43266-0423

Oklahoma

Aging Services Division .... (405) 521-2327
Dept. of Human Services, 312 NE 28th St., Oklahoma City, OK 73125

Adult Protective Services/ Geriatric Care ...... (405) 521-4214 *or* 521-3440 *or* 521-3660
Division of Services for the Aging, Dept. of Human Services, 312 N.E. 28th St., Oklahoma City, OK 73105

Elder Abuse Hotline .... In-State: (800) 522-3511

Oregon

Seniors & People with Disabilities .... (503) 945-5811
500 Summer St., NE, 3rd Fl., Salem, OR 97310-1073

Abuse and Protective Services .... (503) 378-3751
Senior Services Division, Dept. of Human Resources, 313 Public Service Bldg., Salem, OR 97310

Pennsylvania

Department of Aging .... (717) 783-1550
Commonwealth of Pennsylvania, Forum Place, 555 Walnut, 5th Floor, Harrisburg, PA 17101-1919

Fraud and Abuse Hotline .... In-State: (800) 992-2433

Puerto Rico

Governor's Office of Elderly Affairs .... (787) 721-5710
P.O. Box 50063, Old San Juan Station, PR 00902

Rhode Island

Department of Elderly Affairs .... (401) 222-2858
160 Pine St., Providence, RI 02903-3708

Adult Services .... (401) 462-2121
Dept. of Human Services, 600 New London Ave., Cranston, RI 02920

Samoa (American)

Territorial Administration on Aging 011 (684) 633-2207
Government of American Samoa, Pago Pago, AS 96799

South Carolina

Senior and Long Term Care Services .... (803) 898-2501
P.O. Box 8206, Columbia, SC 29202-8206

Division of Adult Services .... (803) 734-5730
Office of Children, Family and Adult Services, Dept. of Social Services, P. O. Box 1520, Columbia, SC 29202-1520

South Dakota

Office of Adult Services and Aging .... (605) 773-3656
700 Governor's Drive, Richard F. Kneip Bldg., Pierre, SD 57501-2291

Tennessee

Commission on Aging & Disability .... (615) 741-2056
Andrew Jackson Bldg., 9th Fl., 500 Deadrick St., Nashville, TN 37243-0860

Adult Protective Services .... (615) 741-5926
Social Services Programs, Dept. of Human Services, Citizens Plaza, 400 Deaderick St., Nashville, TN 37219

Texas

Department of Aging .... (512) 424-6840
4900 North Lamar, 4th Fl., Austin, TX 78751-2316

Texas (continued)

Adult Protective Services ...... (512) 438-3011
Dept. of Human Services, P. O. Box 149030, Austin, TX 78714

Federated States of Micronesia

State Agency on Aging ...... (691) 320-2733
Office of Health Services, Ponape, E.C.I., FM 96941

Utah

Division of Aging and Adult Services ...... (801) 539-3910
120 North 200 West, P.O. Box 45500, Salt Lake City, UT 84145-0500

Vermont

Department of Aging & Disabilities ...... (802) 241-2400
Waterbury Complex, 103 S. Main St., Waterbury, VT 05671-2301

Adult Protective Services ...... (802) 241-2131
Division of Social Services, Dept. of Social & Rehabilitation Services, 103 S. Main St., Waterbury, VT 05676

Virginia

Department for the Aging ...... (804) 662-9333
1600 Forest, Ste. 102, Richmond, VA 23229

Adult Protective Services ...... (804) 662-9241
Bureau of Adult & Family Services, Division of Service Programs, Dept. of Social Services, 8007 Discovery Drive, Richmond, VA 23229-8699

Virgin Islands

Senior Citizen Affairs Division ...... (340) 774-0930
Dept. of Human Services, Knud Hansen Complex, Bldg. A, Charlotte Amalie, VI 00802

Division of Adult Services ...... (809) 774-0930
Dept. of Human Services, Barbel Plaza South, St. Thomas, VI 00802

Washington

Aging & Adult Services Administration ...... (360) 725-2310
Dept. of Social & Health Services, P. O. Box 45050, Olympia, WA 98504-5050

Adult Protective Services Program ...... (206) 753-5227
Aging and Adult Services, Dept. of Social & Health Services, 623 8th S.E., Olympia, WA 98504-0095

West Virginia

Bureau of Senior Citizens ...... (304) 558-3317
Holly Grove- Bldg. 10, 1900 Kanawha Blvd. E., Charleston, WV 25305

Services to the Aged, Blind and Disabled ...... (304) 348-7980
Social Services Bureau, Dept. of Human Services, State Capitol Complex, Bldg. 6, Room B850, Charleston, WV 25305

Wisconsin

Department of Health & Family Services ...... (608) 266-2536
1 West Wilson St, Rm 450, Madison, WI 53707-7850

Wyoming

Division on Aging ...... (307) 777-7986
6101 Yellowstone Rd., Suite 259B, Cheyenne, WY 82002-0710

Family Services ...... (307) 777-6095
Division of Public Assistance & Social Services, Dept. of Health & Social Services, Hathaway Bldg., Cheyenne, WY 82002-0710

XI.

MEDICAID: A MIDDLE-CLASS FINANCIAL OPTION?

THE 1989 repeal of the Medicare Catastrophic Coverage Act opened the door to vastly increased enrollment of otherwise "middle-class" beneficiaries in the Federal-State cosponsored Medicaid programs originally intended to provide care for only the neediest patients. Amendments to the Medicaid Law in 1993 and the Health Insurance Portability and Accountability Act, signed in August 1996 and amended in the Balanced Budget Act, effective August 1997, have complicated this somewhat by changing rules and criminalizing some activities, but middle-class use of Medicaid for long-term care is not likely to be significantly reduced.

Medicaid plays a substantial role in financing long-long term care. The program pays for an average of 46 percent of all care provided in nursing homes and by home health services. Data for 1998 show that Medicaid payments for custodial nursing care and home health care totaled roughly $35 billion for the more than 2.8 million recipients of these services—an average expenditure of about $12,500 per long-term recipient. Only 11 percent of Medicaid beneficiaries are elderly, but because their care is expensive, they account for 31 percent of costs. Not surprisingly, then, with an aging population, long-term care payments play an increasingly larger role in total Medicaid spending and are already the program's largest single cost.

Overall, Medicaid costs grew some 11 percent in 2001. Meanwhile, the recession cut revenues and pushed more personal incomes below state eligibility thresholds. With Medicaid accounting for the largest expenditure in state budgets next to education (an average of 20 percent), states are contemplating eligibility and benefit cuts to reduce the strain on already tight budgets.

Lobbyists for the elderly have long insisted that the potential costs of long-term nursing or custodial care pose the single largest potential financial risk to most retirees of average means. Indeed, the cost of a year's stay in a nursing home averaged $56,000 nationwide in 2001. On the high end, New York and Connecticut averaged over $90,000. The savings of over two-thirds of current nursing home residents are totally depleted within 24 months of their admission. Elder advocates have publicized such data and vigorously lobbied for *Medicare* coverage for long-term custodial care to no avail. Understandably, many retirees are concerned that nursing home costs could quickly wipe them out. However, as explained in Chapter IX, only a relatively small proportion of the elderly face lengthy confinement in a nursing home. Even so, fear of nursing home costs has spawned a new area of financial planning, as described below.

The 1989 Medicare legislation that repealed the Catastrophic Coverage Act also rescinded most of the prohibitions against so-called Medicaid trusts, which permit retirees to become eligible for Medicaid's nursing home coverage without dissipating their estates and provided at-home spouses of institutionalized Medicaid patients with substantial protection against impoverishment. The apparent result has been a proliferation both of attorneys who specialize in drafting Medicaid trusts that meet the technical requirements of the law and of middle-class clients who want their wealth sheltered in the event they need long-term care.

The liberalized treatment of trust arrangements designed to promote Medicaid eligibility was reportedly a compromise intended to offset in part the effects of the repeal of Medicare's catastrophic coverage provisions and to provide some relief for those forced to enter nursing homes. From the perspective of Washington lawmakers, it also achieved another goal. Unlike Medicare, which is Federally funded, a substantial portion of Medicaid costs are funded by *state* taxes. In effect, by limiting Medicare catastrophic illness and long-term care coverage while relaxing middle-class prohibitions on Medicaid eligibility, Congress shifted a portion of the costs of such programs onto the states.

The liberalization of Medicaid eligibility has been somewhat reversed over the past decade. The 1993 Amendments to the Medicaid Law require states to remove the cap on the penalty for transferring assets at less than market value for the purpose of becoming eligible for Medicaid. The penalty is calculated by dividing the value of the transferred assets by the average monthly private pay rate for nursing facilities in the particular state. The result is the number of months of Medicaid ineligibility. The 1989 legislation had capped this period of ineligibility at 30 months; the 1993 legislation removed the cap. The law also requires states to increase the "lookback" period over which they can check for such transfers of assets to three years for transfers to individuals and to five years for transfers to certain types of trusts.

The Health Insurance Portability and Accountability Act (1996), also known as the Kassebaum-Kennedy health reform bill, made asset transfers to qualify for Medicaid for nursing home or other long-term care a federal crime in addition to the penalties described above. This provision passed with no hearings and no debate. Not one House member claimed authorship. The provision, dubbed the "Granny Goes to Jail Law," was poorly drafted and unclear on many issues, such as who might be prosecuted and whether the crime involved was a felony or misdemeanor.

The Balanced Budget Act of 1997 applied the criminal penalties of the "Granny" provision only to those who "for a fee, counsel or assist an individual to make certain transfers of assets" for the purpose of qualifying for Medicaid. This law, dubbed the "Granny's Lawyer Goes to Jail Law," came under immediate fire. In 1998, U.S. Attorney General Janet Reno stated that she would not enforce the law. Later, the New York State Bar Association challenged the law's constitutionality and won a nationwide injunction against its enforcement. The Justice Department filed a notice of appeal that was ultimately withdrawn.

In any event, one should not apply for Medicaid until at least three years after transfers to individuals and five years after transfers to some trusts. Application during these look-back periods may result in penalties under the new periods of ineligibility and possible criminal action against paid advisers. This area of legislation could change frequently over the next few years. For current information on Medicaid and other legal issues for elders, contact the National Senior Citizens Law Center, 1101 14th Street NW, Suite 400, Washington, DC 20005; phone (202) 289-6976; website www.nsclc.org.

Ironically, the recent legislation, instead of discouraging such asset shifting, may encourage more and earlier transfers. The new difference in look-back periods, three years for transfers to individuals and five years for transfers to trusts, may also encourage relatively more transfers to individuals rather than to trusts. However, consider that a significant proportion of nursing home residents recover enough to return home. If these people have intentionally impoverished themselves to qualify for Medicaid, they may now be unable to support themselves or find themselves at the mercy of the beneficiaries of their transferred wealth.

Comprehensive Medicaid Coverage

Medicaid coverage for medical services varies markedly (in amount, duration, and scope) from state to state, within the range of Federal Medicaid standards. All states are required to provide "core" coverage for a variety of services, including inpatient and outpatient hospital services, laboratory and x-ray services, skilled nursing facility services, physicians' and some dentists' services, home health care, medical supplies and appliances, physical and occupational therapy, and speech pathology and audiology services. In addition, all states must pay the transportation costs of Medicaid recipients for travel to and from their health care providers. Many states also include coverage for services of chiropractors, optometrists, podiatrists, private nurses, dental care (including dentures), eyeglasses, and prescription drugs.

Even Medicare's "core" coverage is substantially greater than that offered to Medicare subscribers or to holders even of the costliest Medicare supplemental insurance policies. In most states, Medicaid beneficiaries receive virtually all medical goods and services, even peripheral ones, free of charge. Most pertinent for this discussion, Medicaid pays for the costs of custodial nursing home care once certain income and asset criteria are met.

Not all physicians and health care institutions, including the better-rated nursing facilities, will take Medicaid patients. Thus, many impoverished Medicaid recipients have been forced to accept treatment at substandard "Medicaid clinics" and have ended up at "Medicaid mill" nursing homes. However, in the case of middle-class retirees whose financial plans include the deliberate transfer of assets and "spend downs" to qualify for Medicaid coverage, nursing home admission can be made on a private-payment basis and the "cold-shoulder" treatment usually reserved for destitute Medicaid patients avoided.

Medicaid Eligibility Requirements

Each state determines its own Medicaid eligibility requirements within broad Federal guidelines. Policies are complex and vary considerably from state to state; e.g., a person eligible for Medicaid in one state may not be eligible in another. Furthermore, rules governing both eligibility and services can change during the year in any state.

Generally, states are required to provide Medicaid services to most recipients of Federal and/or state income assistance or related programs. Recipients who in most states automatically qualify for Medicaid include those receiving Aid to Families with Dependent Children (AFDC), Supplemental Security Income (SSI), and certain Medicare beneficiaries (discussed below). States may also provide Medicaid coverage for a variety of "categorically needy" groups, including infants and pregnant women whose family income is at or below 185 percent of the Federal poverty level; aged, blind, or disabled adults whose incomes and assets may be above the SSI threshold but below the Federal poverty level; institutionalized persons with income and resources below specified limits; and "medically needy" persons.

Some aged, blind, and disabled persons are covered under both Medicare and Medicaid as "dual beneficiaries" whose Medicare Part B premiums and Medicare coinsurance are paid by Medicaid. Dual beneficiaries also receive some, but not all, of the more-comprehensive Medicaid coverage described above, including eyeglasses and hearing aids. Such "qualified Medicare beneficiaries" are individuals with incomes at or below the Federal poverty level and resources at or below twice the standard allowed under the SSI program. Based on those criteria, Medicare beneficiaries 65 years or over become eligible for Medicaid in 2002 when countable income falls below $8,860 per year for a single individual and $11,940 for a couple and countable assets do not exceed $2,000 for an individual.

Not all income is included in countable income and certain assets are exempt from the inventory of resources. For example, a spouse confined to a nursing home in 2002 may deduct from monthly income at least $30 for personal needs, a $1,452 to $2,232 monthly allowance for the at-home spouse, and an allowance for each additional family member of at least one-third of the allowance for the at-home spouse. An individual's or couple's home, automobile (up to a certain value), household goods and personal effects of "reasonable" value, and burial plots and life insurance with a face value up to $1,500 or burial funds up to $1,500 are exempt assets. The "spousal impoverishment protection" provisions of the 1989 repeal of the Medicare Catastrophic Coverage Act entitle the at-home spouse to retain, in 2002, a minimum of $17,856 or one-half of the couple's total resources up to a maximum of $89,280 and protect exempt assets (car, household goods, and personal effects) to *any* value.

In short, current legislation provides liberal exemptions of both income and assets from Medicaid eligibility tests. Today, many of the middle-class aged may qualify for Medicaid and still retain substantial income and resources, especially if a couple's liquid assets (bank accounts, CDs, stocks, bonds) are converted into exempt assets and a portion of them—sufficient to produce income up to the Medicaid limits—annuitized.

Asset Conversion

For couples with liquid assets under $350,000 or so, the least involved and least costly way to protect financial resources from Medicaid "spend down" requirements is to convert them to exempt-category assets. For example, all outstanding debt should be paid at once. If a couple's home has a mortgage, nonexempt assets held in savings accounts, stocks, and bonds can be used to pay off the outstanding mortgage balance, which immediately converts those funds to an exempt category, the home. If the couple rents but has substantial savings, the savings can be used to purchase a condominium home that will be exempt. Or if the family car needs replacing, nonexempt resources could be used to purchase a new one, which would be exempt under the spousal impoverishment protection legislation.

Similarly, liquid assets can be used to make home improvements or to purchase household goods that are exempt from Medicaid resource limitations. Preventive and cost-saving home repairs can be made that would be prohibitively expensive under Medicaid's income limitations. These could include a new roof, siding, windows, plumbing and heating, wiring, insulation, or energy-efficient labor saving appliances that reduce living costs for the at-home spouse. Even major remodeling such as a new kitchen or bathrooms, additions to the structure, or low-maintenance landscaping might be contemplated as a means of protecting assets while making life easier for the spouse at home.

And by annuitizing remaining liquid assets, a portion of otherwise countable financial resources can be converted into largely, perhaps totally, exempt income. At current annuity rates, a $100,000 lifetime annuity purchased at age 65 would yield an income of about $8,300 per year to an at-home female spouse—$10,500 per year if aged 75.

Exempt assets lose that status when the institutionalized beneficiary dies, and states may (but are not required to) seek reimbursement for Medicaid outlays for nursing home expenses from the recipient's estate. In this connection, Medicaid authorities are sometimes granted a lien against the home. Therefore, pouring assets into the family home provides protection only so long as the at-home spouse or certain other relations reside there. After the spouse or other relations vacate the residence or die, the state may seek recovery of expenses after the death of the institutionalized beneficiary—unless the property has been transferred outright to another party, such as the heirs.

Never attempt asset conversion for the purpose of meeting Medicaid eligibility without first consulting an attorney and accountant who specialize in this area and who are familiar with the laws in your state. Of course, the establishment of a Medicaid trust, described next, will also require professional counsel.

Medicaid Trusts

If total countable assets exceed Medicaid limits even after the above measures have been taken, they now can still be sheltered using so-called Medicaid trusts. Within certain look-back periods, Medicaid law does not permit individuals to transfer assets to individuals or to a trust in order to qualify under Medicaid's income and resource limits. Federal law requires that states "look back" at least three years for transfers of assets to individuals (and some trusts) and at least five years for transfers of assets to certain trusts. Once the look-back period ends, however, the grantor can become eligible for Medicaid coverage.

Medicaid trusts became big business during the past decade. Reportedly, "elder-practice" law firms in the larger metropolitan areas regularly hosted Medicaid trust promotions for senior citizen audiences, hoping to drum up clients. For legal fees of around $2,500 or $3,500, such firms will draft a trust agreement that meets Medicaid

127

qualifications.

Medicaid trusts usually are irrevocable trust agreements with special provisions added to satisfy the needs of long-term care patients and the requirements of the Medicaid authorities. Although individual circumstances make each agreement unique, Medicaid trusts generally have had two common characteristics: (1) they require that income from the trust, or trust principal as required, be used to pay the costs of long-term nursing care during periods of ineligibility, and (2) they are designed so that countable income from the trust, including outside buildup, does not exceed Medicaid limits. (Thus, trust assets could be limited to low-income or no-income holdings.) Such provisions could be made through a "springing trust" arrangement in which a *revocable* trust agreement, which retains complete control of trust assets until the last minute, would automatically become an *irrevocable* Medicaid trust when the grantor enters a nursing home. Trusts agreements are, no doubt, being modified as needed to conform to the new legal requirements.

A Public-Private Medicaid "Partnership"?

The increased use of Medicaid by the middle-class has prompted officials in some states to look for ways to reduce the consequent financial strain on state budgets. In one current "experiment," a public-private "partnership" provides incentives for elderly persons to purchase private long-term care insurance in return for the state's promise to waive Medicaid eligibility spend-down requirements for nursing home costs when private insurance benefits cease. Called the "Partnership for Long-Term Care," California, Connecticut, Indiana, and New York are participating in the experiment as of 2002 under a grant from the Robert Wood Johnson Foundation Program to Promote Long-Term Care Insurance for the Elderly. If successful, the program could be adopted by the other states.

The New York plan clearly states that the desired market is primarily the middle-class elderly—single persons with a total income of at least $30,000 per year and assets of at least $60,000 (excluding home) and married persons with yearly incomes between $40,000 and $50,000 and assets over $140,000. Individuals must purchase and maintain in force an approved private long-term care policy that promises to pay benefits for nursing home care for 3 years, for home care for 6 years, or for an equivalent combination of both. In return,

New York will disregard assets (but not income) when determining Medicaid eligibility.

For more information, write to the Partnership for Long-Term Care, National Program Office, University of Maryland Center of Aging, 1240 HHP Building, College Park, MD 20742-2611, call 301-405-7555, or visit www.hhp.umd.edu/AGING/.

Must We All Become Thieves?

Medicaid never was intended to be a financial tool of the middle class. It was designed to provide medical relief to the genuinely needy. Yet today, some middle-class retirees who would never "steal" from their neighbors are taking advantage of Medicaid trusts to protect their personal wealth at the expense of other taxpayers.

Defenders of Medicaid trusts as a legal means to preserve one's hard-earned wealth claim their effect is identical to tax shelters, which permit some to pay less tax than others who deploy their assets in less-advantaged ways. Still others argue that by entering the Medicaid rolls, they simply are seeking partial restitution for the government's prior confiscation of their wealth that has funded programs that almost surely will impoverish their children and grandchildren unless they preserve their inheritance.

From a purely ethical standpoint, it may be difficult for most people to distinguish the "right" from the "wrong" in any of these positions. Rather, it would seem that questions of who are the "more deserving" are largely political and are incapable of final resolution. What is clearer is that many no doubt *will* take advantage of all legal means to prevent the dissipation of their wealth. The inexorable result is the tendency to make "suckers" of anyone who does not do likewise, even if he or she is in general sympathy with the original goals of programs such as Medicaid.

This process appears to be characteristic of almost any regime that seeks to advantage some people at the expense of others. Seemingly, those who are disadvantaged eventually seek redress by one means or another, usually by demanding "benefits" for themselves. The result effectively defeats the original intent of the program.

129

Part 4

END-OF-LIFE DECISIONS

XII.

LEGAL CONSIDERATIONS

O F great concern to many older people is the possibility that if they become irreversibly ill and are unable to make decisions for themselves, artificial means will be used to prolong their lives long after they have any hope of recovery and long after they would wish to remain "alive" were they able to speak for themselves. Not only does such treatment often prolong the anguish of family and friends, but it also can be financially devastating to the survivors who may be forced to pay the costs of such care.

In today's litigious society, however, virtually no care provider—hospital, nursing home, or physician—is willing to accept the potential liability for withholding life-prolonging care. This is so even when a patient's life is being sustained under highly artificial circumstances and where there is no hope of recovery. The only way to insure that your wishes are carried out is to state your instructions in writing according to the procedures required by the pertinent laws of the state in which you reside.

Living Wills

All 50 states and the District of Columbia have enacted "living will" laws that specify the legal language individuals must follow in declaring their wishes with respect to medical treatment in the event they should become unable to make decisions. In some states it is not necessary to have a lawyer draw up a living will. However, you must use the form that has been approved for use in your state. To obtain a copy of a living will form for your state, see your attorney or send for your state's advance directive package and the booklet, "Advance Directives and End-of-Life Decisions" ($5.95) from Partnership for Caring (formerly Choice in Dying), 1620 Eye Street NW, Suite 202, Washington DC 20006; 1-800-989-WILL (9455); or www.partnershipforcaring.org. See also, "Consumer's Tool Kit for Health Care Advance Planning" from the American Bar Association at www.abanet.org/aging/toolkit/home.htm. The ABA can also be reached at 740 Fifteenth Street NW, Washington DC 20005-1019. Tel: 202-662-1000.

You should also ask your doctors and local hospital for a copy of any form to which they require a living will to adhere before they will honor its instructions.

LIVING WILL DECLARATION

To My Family Doctors, and All Those Concerned with My Care

I, ... , being of sound mind, make this statement as a directive to be followed if I become unable to participate in decisions regarding my medical care.

If I should be in an incurable or irreversible mental or physical condition with no reasonable expectation of recovery, I direct my attending physician to withhold or withdraw treatment that merely prolongs my dying. I further direct that treatment be limited to measures to keep me comfortable and to relieve pain.

These directions express my right to refuse treatment. Therefore I expect my family, doctor, and everyone concerned with my care to regard themselves as legally and morally bound to act in accord with my wishes, and in so doing to be free of any legal liability for having followed my direction.

I especially do not want: _____

Other instructions/comments _____

Proxy designation clause: Should I become unable to communicate my instructions as stated above, I designate the following person to act in my behalf:

Name: _____

Address: _____

If the person I have named is unable to act in my behalf, I authorize the following person to do so:

Name: _____

Address: _____

Signed: _____   Date: _____

Witness: (Name & Address)   Witness: (Name & Address)

All living wills must be signed and witnessed, and it is prudent (and may be required by law) to have such documents notarized as well. Witnesses to a living will may not be anyone who would "benefit" from your death through an inheritance or otherwise. Usually the following individuals are specifically prohibited by statute from witnessing a living will: anyone related to the declarant by blood or marriage; any heir or claimant to any part of the declarant's estate, including creditors; the declarant's physician or physician's employee; any employee of the patient's health facility; or any other person responsible for the patient's health care.

Once the living will is prepared, you should keep the original with your personal papers. You should give copies to your doctors, members of your family, and your health care proxy (discussed in the next section). Some states require that a living will be updated periodically. Even if your state does not, you should review the living will periodically to make sure that it still accurately states your wishes and initial and date it to so indicate.

In some states the prescribed form must be followed precisely. Other states permit personalized instructions. The contents of the living will in these states will differ for each individual depending on his or her wishes with respect to certain medical circumstances, including "hydration" and "feeding," that *must* be specified in the document. Prescribed forms are not intended to be used as "finished documents," but only as starting points for drafting a living will in consultation with your attorney and other interested parties.

In states that do not have a prescribed form, living will declarations should be drafted to meet the requirements of health care providers and other pertinent law. On the previous page is a sample form that has been widely distributed in those states and may serve as a foundation for a living will declaration (and health care proxy) in consultation with your attorney and health care providers. In some states, such as New Jersey, attorneys have available a lengthy living will form that accommodates that state's relatively lengthy, comprehensive law respecting refusal of life-supporting medical care.

Durable Powers of Attorney for Health Care
(Health Care Proxies)

Many health care analysts advise that a durable power of attorney

HEALTH CARE PROXY

1. I, ... *(name)*......... , hereby appoint ....*(name, home address, telephone number)*............ as my health care agent to make any and all health care decisions for me, except to the extent that I state otherwise. This proxy shall take effect when and if I become unable to make my own health care decisions.

2. Optional instructions: I direct my agent to make health care decisions in accord with my wishes and limitations as stated below, or as he or she otherwise knows. _____

_____

3. Name of substitute or fill-in agent if the person I appoint above is unable, unwilling, or unavailable to act as my health care agent. ....*(Name, home address, telephone number.)*.........

4. Unless I revoke it, this proxy shall remain in effect indefinitely, or until the date or conditions stated here: _____

_____

5. Signature, address and date _____

Witness: (name and address)   Witness: (name and address)

The proxy may not be a witness, and the two witnesses must be individuals who do not stand to benefit from the death of the proxy maker; both must be 18 or older.

for health care (health care proxy) should accompany the living will. The specified living will forms in some states include such a health care proxy and should be used when available.

In brief, a durable power of attorney for health care empowers someone of your choosing to act in your behalf should you become unable to make decisions for yourself. Plainly, you should choose your surrogate carefully and thoroughly discuss with him or her your wishes as expressed in your living will, even if that requires going into specific detail about precise procedures and under precisely which circumstances you do or do not wish them to be used. In most states and the District of Columbia, health care proxies are permitted to make medical decisions specifically including decisions to withdraw or withhold life support. However, in some states the force of health care proxies is limited to one degree or another. Nevertheless, a health care proxy who also is supported by a properly drafted living will declaration is in a strong position to see that your wishes are carried out.

As with living wills, the legal forms for health care proxies vary from state to state. You should use the form that is specified by your state. These forms are available from Partnership for Caring, cited above. A sample health care proxy that may serve as a rough example is printed on the previous page. This form should not be used as your living will.

Since the issues may be complex, it is important that individuals determine their wishes with respect to end-of-life medical treatment while they are still able and discuss them with the physician, loved ones, and health care proxy. Even the most carefully prepared documents cannot guarantee that all your wishes will be carried out. However, if you have not prepared a living will or a health care proxy, it is almost guaranteed that they will *not* be.

XIII.

FUNERAL OPTIONS

DEATH is one of the few events that every human experiences. Nevertheless, the disposition of a person's physical remains often is one of the least-planned of his or her affairs. Fears about death understandably may make all concerned, especially family members, reluctant to discuss or plan funeral arrangements much in advance of actual need. However, "last minute" arrangements made in hastened or anguished circumstances can be far more costly—sometimes onerously so to survivors—than informed decisions reached before death stares one in the face. As a practical matter, the disposition of one's physical remains might prudently be arranged just as one plans for the disposition of one's legal estate.

Many funeral options are available. Some people derive satisfaction knowing that after they die they will be celebrated by a funeral that spares no expense and is attended by a host of friends and family. Others desire a private funeral of modest proportions that does not pose a financial burden to survivors or deplete the estate that will pass to heirs. Still others prefer that no funeral service be held, and that their remains be disposed of in the least costly fashion. Your own wishes probably will not be fulfilled unless you make them known—and unless you review the options available for a particular type of funeral arrangement.

Funeral Regulations

Whatever those wishes may be, a variety of state and Federal laws regulate funeral practice. It is in your interest and the interest of your survivors to be familiar with the principal laws governing the disposition of human remains and funeral industry operations. The Federal Trade Commission's "Funeral Rule" (16 CFR Part 453) governs disclosure regarding funeral costs. Among other provisions, the Funeral Rule requires that funeral providers give price information over the telephone and that they supply, on request, a general price list of all items and services offered. These rules protect consumers from the subtle pressure tactics sometimes employed in a face-to-face meeting with funeral personnel.

The Funeral Rule also requires that customers be given information about embalming and specifies that funeral providers must not falsely state that embalming is required by law; must disclose in writing (with some exceptions) when embalming is *not* required by law; may not charge a fee for unauthorized embalming unless it is required by law; disclose in writing that (usually) you have the right to choose between cremation or immediate burial if you do not want embalming; and disclose in writing under what circumstances embalming is a practical necessity.

The Funeral Rule stipulates that funeral providers disclose any fees that they charge for so-called cash advance items related to funeral arrangements. These are items or services, including flowers, obituary notices, clergy honoraria, and the like, that the funeral director purchases in your behalf but that you could purchase yourself. The Funeral Rule requires that the provider inform you if a fee is added to the price of cash advance items or if the provider gets a kickback from any of the suppliers.

One of the most costly items in most funerals is the casket. However, in some circumstances a casket may not be appropriate. For consumers who select direct cremation, for example, an inexpensive alternative container or unfinished wood box that will be destroyed during cremation may suffice. Under the Funeral Rule, funeral directors who offer cremation services are prohibited from telling you that state or local law requires a casket for direct cremations and must make an unfinished wood box or alternative container available.

The variety of conventional funeral options could bewilder your survivors. It is not much trouble to telephone one or more funeral providers in your locality, listed under "Funeral Homes" in the Yellow Pages, to request a "general price list" of funeral items and services. Check the items you want and discuss them with those who will arrange your funeral. A copy of the list, with your written instructions, ought to be readily available to your spouse or anyone else who may require such information upon your death.

For further information on the laws governing funerals in your state, how to make funeral arrangements, or the options available, contact Funeral Consumers Alliance, P.O. Box 10, Hinesburg, VT 05461, (802) 482-3437, www.funerals.org. The alliance, a federation of nonprofit consumer information societies that encourages advance planning and cost efficiency, informs consumers about alternatives for funeral or nonfuneral dispositions. The Cremation Association of North America, 401 North Michigan Avenue, Chicago IL 60611, (312) 644-6610, www.cremationassociation.org is an association of 750 crematories, cemeteries, and funeral homes that offer cremation. The National Research and Information Center, 2250 E. Devon Avenue, Suite 250, Des Plaines, IL 60018; (800) 662-7666 offers a Funeral Service Consumer Assistance Program, with information on death, grief, and funerals.

A free copy of "Funerals: A Consumer Guide" and additional information concerning the Funeral Rule are available on the FTC website at www.ftc.gov. You may also telephone or write Consumer Response Center, Federal Trade Commission, 600 Pennsylvania, NW, Room H-130, Washington, DC 20580-0001; 1-877-FTC-HELP (1-877-382-4357).

Pre-Paid Funerals

Many funeral directors urge consumers to pay for their own funerals in advance—termed "pre-need"—which they say will not only save grief-stricken survivors the trouble of making funeral arrangements but also will save money by locking-in the current price for funeral goods and services.

In principle this may seem prudent. In practice it requires that consumers take a number of precautions to insure that they actually get the funeral they purchased. Reportedly, in a number of instances, prepaid funeral funds have gone not into a trust account or life insurance policy but into a managed-money account to which the funeral director may have direct access. In several instances, the funeral director has used the funds for other purposes or the managed accounts have gone bankrupt.

If you are considering prepaid funeral arrangements, you should determine how your funds will be held in trust. If they are not placed in an escrow account, trust account, or life insurance policy to which the funeral firm does not have access, do not do business with that firm.

Equally important, make sure that you can get a refund if you change your mind. Where funds are held in a deposit fund or trust account at a financial institution, you should be able to receive a refund in accordance with the terms of the written contract (there probably will be a penalty for early withdrawal). If the funds are poured into a life insurance or annuity contract, the terms of the prepaid arrangement should permit you to receive the cash surrender value of the contract.

Burial Insurance

You can prefund your own funeral, to be carried out according to your instructions, by purchasing a life insurance policy with a death benefit adequate to cover the costs of the funeral you desire. As with prepaid funeral arrangements, prefunding can save your survivors the expense of your funeral. Although it does not relieve your survivors of all funeral tasks, such a plan will insure that the funds are available when needed—and could cost substantially less than the prepaid funeral, depending on the premiums that you must pay to keep the insurance in force before you die. For example, if you purchase a level-premium policy and die shortly after the policy becomes effective, your estate probably will save much of the cost of your funeral. Of course, you have to qualify for life insurance. If you are in poor health, you may not be able to get insurance or the death benefit may not justify the premium costs.

Low-Cost or No-Cost Alternatives

Those who do not want a conventional funeral might consider legal nonfuneral options. In addition to burial, entombment, and cremation, human remains can be disposed of legally via donation for scientific study. Many large medical centers accept donations of human remains for purposes of teaching or research. In most instances the facility will pay a donation fee upon receipt of the remains. In many states, such donations are regulated by a state Anatomical Board that pays the fees to the donor's estate, which then can either be retained as part of the estate or donated to a designated charity. For information, forms, and procedures, contact the medical facility to which you wish to donate your remains. All such donations are revocable by alternate instructions prior to death.

At least one nonfuneral cremation plan will, at a significantly lower cost than conventional funerals and burials, transport the remains from the place of death anywhere in the United States to a holding facility pending procurement of the signed death certificate and disposition permit; cremate and scatter the remains by sea, rose garden, or return to the family, as desired; and supply urn and professional and administrative services as needed. For further information, contact The Neptune Society, 4312 Woodman Avenue, Third Floor, Sherman Oaks, California 91423; (888) 637-8863; www.neptunesociety.com. This is a for-profit firm with offices in nine states.

Finally, in some states, such as Texas, a family may bury its own dead without using a licensed funeral director. Do-it-yourself burials require at minimum a statement of death, death certificate, and burial-transit permit. In many states, local ordinances govern do-it-yourself burials, which may be prohibited in some jurisdictions. To obtain information about laws governing funerals by nonlicensed family members, contact the Funeral Consumers Alliance, cited above.

Appendix
A PARTING THOUGHT ON PUBLIC HEALTH CARE

POPULAR sentiment in favor of some type of socialized health insurance evidently flourishes in the United States today. For example, to the extent that there is dissatisfaction among the elderly with Medicare, it is chiefly becuase it is said to be "too costly" and affords "too few benefits." There is strong political pressure to add new benefits, especially prescription drug coverage. Some proposals woudl offer this coverage to all Medicare beneficiaries regardless of their income or wealth. Given the political clout of the elderly, it seems very unlikely that nominal Medicare benefits will be *reduced* anytime soon (though *actual* benefits may continue to be curtailed through reduced reimbursements under the DRG and relative value scale payment policies.)

At the same time, there appears to be growing public recognition that the present arrangement places an unfair burden on others. For example, families with young children, who are thought to be just as deserving of access to health care as are either the elderly or Medicaid recipients who pay nothing for their care, are disadvantaged under the present system. Today, many are forced to contribute precious financial resources for the care of others while they themselves must go without.

An evidently growing segment of the public believes that an equitable solution to this disparate treatment is a publicly financed universal health care system that would favor no class of beneficiaries over any other and, it is thought, would be less costly than either the current "patchwork" health care arrangements or a purely market-based regime. As appealing as it may seem at first blush, from the perspective of both sound economics and social ethics, there would appear to be many difficulties with this approach.

Health Care Spending in Perspective

One of the principal advantages a publicly financed health care system is said to have over a market-based system is that a public system would be better equipped to "contain costs." As a primary example of the deficiencies of market-based medicine, advocates of universal health insurance cite that, as a percent of Gross Domestic

Product (GDP), health care expenditures in the United States are greater than in any other major industrialized nation—and still are increasing.

Although the numbers may be accurate, the argument is spurious. A relatively high level of spending *per se* in no way reflects "deficiencies" in the way health care is provided. From a market perspective there is no rationale for believing that *any* particular level of health care expenditures represents the optimum. Individuals decide how much they wish to spend on their health in relation to other things, and very often that decision depends on the proportion of their wealth that *must* be spent on life's other necessities—food, shelter, clothing, etc. It is a matter of supposition that in economies where the necessities of life require less of one's resources, a relatively greater proportion will be directed toward improving health and longevity. That the United States spends proportionally more on health care than any other country may indicate not that we somehow have "fallen behind" in managing health care, but that we have advanced economically beyond other nations—to the point that health concerns are markedly greater priorities here than elsewhere.

Hence, that we choose to devote more of our resources toward improving our health might reflect our relatively greater affluence. And there is ample reason to suppose that an even greater portion of our resources may be channeled that way in the future, especially if medical advances continue to encourage even greater consumption. Who would not want to invest in the discovery of a fountain of youth, which is what modern medicine in effect promises today? It should come as no surprise that the "product" of medicine in the United States, which has enabled millions to enjoy longer lives in better health than ever before, in recent decades has attained greater appeal in relation to other things.

Or to put it another way, in the last three decades consumer spending on, say, recreational goods and services has increased markedly as a proportion of total spending. Yet no one complains that the relative level of spending on such items as stereos, VCRs, speedboats, or Las Vegas vacations, which is much higher in the United States than in most other countries, is "too high." Why, then, the preoccupation with containing the level of spending on health care, especially when it would seem to mirror priorities that, literally, are healthy ones?

Beyond this, our relatively greater health expenditures also reflect the aging of America and the fact that for the majority of the population life expectancies have increased markedly. In relation to GDP, health care expenditures can be expected to increase disproportionately as the proportion of the elderly and longevity increase. The reason is uncomplicated: the aged contribute proportionally less to the other GDP components than they do to its health care component. (The elderly consume relatively more health services than other age groups at the same time that, as retireds, they contribute less to the nonconsumption components of GDP.) In part, then, our current level of spending on health care has been a predictable result of demographic contours that have little if anything to do with the way the health care markets operate.

Subsidies Create Price Spirals

But perhaps the greatest misunderstanding of health care cost pressures involves the Medicare and Medicaid subsidies. Appeals for greater government intervention in our health care system often lay the blame for "high costs" on mismanaged hospitals, greedy doctors and lawyers (who prosecute malpractice suits), and profit-seeking insurance companies. But the chief culprits are Medicare and Medicaid themselves.

It is an axiom of economics that *subsidies of any kind create shortages that promote price spirals.* Subsidies affect supply, demand, and prices. Agricultural subsidies often involve restrictions on supply as well as "price supports" in the form of government purchases at above-market prices.

In the instances of Medicare and Medicaid, which enlarge demand for medical services, the fully predictable result has been to increase the prices. It would seem that whenever a third party assumes responsibility for payments there is a subsidy effect, with demand tending to increase and prices tending to be pressured upward. For example, it almost surely is not coincidental that with the advent of tax-exempt employer sponsored group health insurance after World War II, health care prices began to increase faster than the prices of other things. Indeed, the prices of health care related goods and services as measured by the Consumer Price Index (CPI) have increased faster than the prices of other goods and services in all but six years since 1947. Medicare hugely increased health-care subsidies to elderly consumers, and the prices of Medicare-covered services skyrocketed after the program was introduced in 1966.

Chart 3 shows the price of a semiprivate hospital room relative to the prices of five other types of health-related goods and services from 1947 to 1995. An increase in the relative price of a hospital room in any given period indicates that the price of the hospital room increased at a faster rate than did the price of the comparison item during that period. The chart shows clearly that the rate of increase

Chart 3
RELATIVE PRICE OF Semiprivate HOSPITAL ROOMS

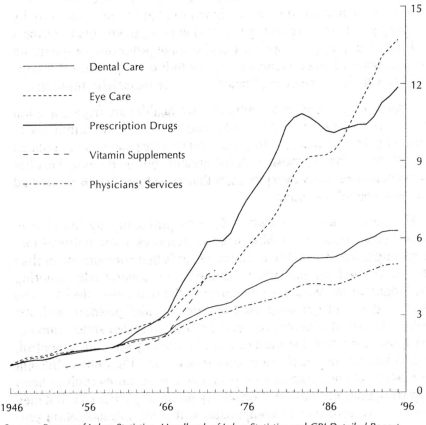

Source: Bureau of Labor Statistics, *Handbook of Labor Statistics* and *CPI Detailed Report.*

in the price of a hospital room accelerated with respect to the rate of increase in the price of four relatively unsubsidized items (dental care, eye care, prescription drugs, and vitamin supplements) precisely at the time Medicare was established in 1966. On the other hand, the rate of increase in the price of hospital rooms accelerated much less, if at all, relative to the rate of increase in the cost of physicians' services that also were subsidized in 1966. That is, the price inflation of subsidized hospital rooms and physicians' services both accelerated relative to the price inflation of unsubsidized items. This is what economic theory would predict, and this is what has happened.

Subsidies Foster Scarcities—and Rationing

Even less well understood by many is the tendency for health care subsidies over the long run to create scarcities. Producer subsidies to farmers or manufacturers are designed to foster scarcity directly by keeping goods from reaching the market (*e.g.*, payments to farmers to keep land idle, grain purchase and storage programs, or quotas on auto imports). But consumer subsidies indirectly produce the same effects, which, in the case of health care, are especially injurious.

Stated simply, consumer subsidies for health care trigger a spiral of events that begins with accelerated demand and culminates in rationing, in which access to goods and services can be manipulated to suit the wishes of those with the greatest political clout. This has happened in virtually every country that has adopted state-sponsored universal health insurance.

Ultimately, access to care is decided politically by the elite in power (one shudders to think what preferences some political factions might legislate). The eventual result is that someone other than the patient and the physician—usually a bureaucrat administering the "regulations" who has no interest in the outcome—decides who does or does not get what kind of care. A chief problem with the politically based allocation of scarce resources is that almost inevitably those resources are used in ways favored by the elite in control, but which may not be (indeed, almost never are) their most effecient use. Medical entitlements to sophisticated procedures such as heart bypass operations may be enormously politically attractive, but they are not cost effective in comparison with, say, immunization programs.

149

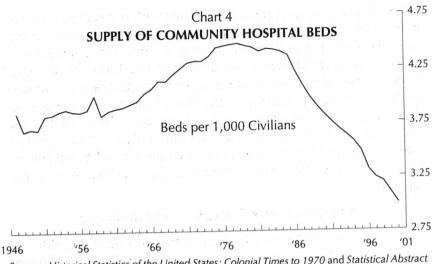

Chart 4
SUPPLY OF COMMUNITY HOSPITAL BEDS

Beds per 1,000 Civilians

4.75
4.25
3.75
3.25
2.75

1946   '56   '66   '76   '86   '96   '01

Source: *Historical Statistics of the United States: Colonial Times to 1970* and *Statistical Abstract of the United States.*

The point is that, wherever resources are scarce, all needs cannot be satisfied, and someone must decide how they will be distributed. In a market-based health care system, those decisions are made by the patient and doctor, who together arrive at the most cost-effective course of treatment within the range of affordability. Under this arrangement, virtually everyone who needs it gets some care. In a socialized health care environment, someone other than the patient or the doctor makes those decisions based on priorities that often are mechanistic and that may deny all care to those who do not meet certain qualifications (say, because you are "too old" or have "no dependents" or are not in a "crucial occupation").

The flip side of this situation is "supply side" scarcity that results from restraints that often are concurrently imposed on the providers of the subsidized goods and services. In the case of Medicare and Medicaid, for example, at least one "cost containment" initiative undertaken in the 1980s appears to have had measurable effects on the supply of one health care commodity. As shown in Chart 4, the supply of community hospital beds has dropped sharply since Medicare's substitution of the DRG prospective payment system for reimbursement of actual charges. (The average length of stay for Medicare patients decreased markedly following the introduction of the DRG system. Under that system, hospitals are paid a fixed fee for a given diagnosis and they benefit financially if actual costs are less than the payment they receive—that is, if patients are discharged quickly.)

Beyond this, regulation of physicians' charges under Medicare's "relative value scale" reimbursement policy almost surely will have unintended consequences over the long run. The reasoning behind the "relative value" policy is roughly as follows: on the basis of the time and resources it takes them to learn their respective specialties and the time they actually spend with patients, some doctors are paid "too much" and some "too little" under market-based pricing, and therefore all doctors' charges should be regulated to reflect more accurately the relative value of their inputs.

Such logic is seriously flawed and betrays a lack of understanding of how prices (doctors' fees) promote self-regulating markets. It appears to depend on the assumption that the current allocation of human resources in the training of physicians reflects "optimal utility." In fact, the very presence of the "imbalances" that the relative value regime seeks to redress is *prima facie* evidence that this cannot be so. The genius of the market is that when some jobs are paid "too much" while others are paid "too little," soon there will be more people available to do the higher paying job. Markets rarely, if ever, reach, let alone sustain, equilibrium. But the continual process of adjustment insures that, all else equal, vast imbalances cannot persist.

To enshrine existing imbalances by way of an income-based policy, which is what the "relative value scale" reimbursement scheme does, is economic insanity. Over the long run, it can be expected to drive talented individuals *away* from those medical occupations that, as evidenced by market prices, are most valued. Indeed, the long-run effects of price restraints, rationing of health care and the concomitant dilution of physician authority, and the many other attributes of politically regulated medicine are not hard to predict: they very likely will drive talented individuals away from medicine. In their most completely developed expression (*i.e.*, in fully socialized medical environments) such restraints have been a powerful prescription for scarcities, even of the most elementary medical goods and services. Reportedly, it was hard to find even a bottle of aspirin in Soviet Russia during its final years.

In a more recent example, Canada, which has essentially eliminated free markets in medical care, has seen its health services become nearly as scarce as Ontario orange groves. Of the industrialized countries that have universal access, publicly-funded health care systems, Canada uniquely bans private medicine, including private insurance and private hospitals that compete for patient demand. And, unlike most other universal access countries, Canada also does not charge user fees, which force health-care consumers to participate in the costs of the care they demand. The Fraser Institute (a Vancouver-based think tank) reports that Canada ranks 17th out of 20 industrialized, universal-access countries in doctors per thousand people. Yet in 1970, the year when public insurance first fully applied to physician services, Canada ranked fourth in that category. Among these same countries, Canadians are most likely to wait more than a month for nonemergency surgery and had the greatest difficulty accessing a specialist. Though Canada is the number one health-care spender among these countries, it ranks 18th out of 23 in access to MRIs and 17th out of 22 in access to CT scanners. The median wait for an MRI from the time of referral was seven months in 2001.

Problems with Health Care "Rights"

Many people apparently believe that equal access to health care is a "right" which everyone in an advanced country such as the United States ought to enjoy. At the very least, however, the notion of rights of any kind requires that they be describable. In the case of health care, this would seem to imply some related level of benefits that is obvious. But it isn't. Some people rush to the doctor for every stubbed toe while others may be on their death beds before they will consent to see a doctor; the hypochondriac demands more care than the Christian Scientist.

As a result, any health care "rights" assigned to individuals with such disparate behavior will, in all likelihood, be viewed differently by their possessors. Some will view their rights far more expansively than others. If health care rights are viewed broadly to include treatment on demand, it is the hypochondriac who will consume scarce resources at the expense of others. If such rights are not so viewed, as they almost certainly would not be, then the problem of rationing is reintroduced, and the "rights" made conditional—which is but another way of saying there are no rights at all.

The larger problem is that human health and human behavior often are directly linked. Of course, many people who are "health conscious" and act in ways to promote their own good health still have heart attacks, get cancer, or suffer illness no matter how assiduously they follow a health regimen. But others by free choice engage in behavior that is known to lead directly to illness or accident. Should others be forced to pay the costs of care of those who persist in behavior that is risky? In this context, health care rights that convey equal access to care, or care on demand, would seem to imply disregard for the possible individual and social advantages of one type of behavior over another. Put another way, they would seem to subsidize pathological behavior which, broadly described, accounts for a substantial portion of health care expenditures in the United States today.

MEDICAL EXPENSE RECORD

| Date | Description of Charges | Amount | MEDICARE PAID | | SUPPLEMENTAL INSURANCE PAID | | PERSONAL PAYMENTS | | |
			Amount	Date	Amount	Date	Balance	Amount Paid	Date

MEDICAL EXPENSE RECORD

Date	Description of Charges	Amount	Medicare Paid		Supplemental Insurance Paid		Personal Payments		
			Amount	Date	Amount	Date	Balance	Amount Paid	Date

MEDICAL EXPENSE RECORD

| Date | Description of Charges | Amount | MEDICARE PAID | | SUPPLEMENTAL INSURANCE PAID | | PERSONAL PAYMENTS | | |
			Amount	Date	Amount	Date	Balance	Amount Paid	Date

MEDICAL EXPENSE RECORD

Date	Description of Charges	Amount	MEDICARE PAID		SUPPLEMENTAL INSURANCE PAID		PERSONAL PAYMENTS		
			Amount	Date	Amount	Date	Balance	Amount Paid	Date

PUBLICATIONS
AND SUSTAINING MEMBERSHIPS

You can receive our twice monthly *Research Reports* and monthly *Economic Education Bulletin* by entering a **Sustaining Membership** for only $16 quarterly or $59 annually. If you wish to receive only the *Economic Education Bulletin*, you may enter an **Education Membership** for $25 annually.

INVESTMENT GUIDE

At your request, AIER will forward your payment for a subscription to the *INVESTMENT GUIDE* published by American Investment Services, Inc. (AIS). The *GUIDE* is issued once a month at a price of $59 per year (add $8 for foreign airmail). It provides guidance to investors, both working and retired, of modest and large means, to help them preserve the real value of their wealth during these difficult financial times. AIS is wholly owned by AIER and is the only investment advisory endorsed by AIER.